TECH TO TECH
An Informational Guide for
HVAC/R Technicians to Increase Their Wage

by

Chris Reak

DORRANCE PUBLISHING CO., INC.
PITTSBURGH, PENNSYLVANIA 15222

ISBN # 0-8059-6287-5
Printed in the United States of America

First Printing

For information or to order additional books, please write:
Dorrance Publishing Co., Inc.
701 Smithfield Street
Third Floor
Pittsburgh, Pennsylvania 15222
U.S.A.
1-800-788-7654
Or visit our web site and on-line catalog at
www.dorrancepublishing.com

CONTENTS

CHAPTER 1

DEFINING THE PROBLEM

The problem with the HVAC/R technician's pay is simple: **The boss does not think the technicians are worth any more.** A company pays a technician exactly what the company believes the technician is worth, and a technician must understand this before wage increases can be *earned*. To earn a wage increase, technicians have to increase their value to the company. In other words, technicians need to prove to the boss they are worth more to the company than they are getting paid and that they are productive for the company. The first step in determining what a technician is financially worth to a company is to determine what the technician's value to the company is.

Here is a technician's day: Get up in the morning, run calls all day, turn in invoices at the end of the day, and go home. Technicians do this all week, then collect a paycheck, deposit it, and start a new week. They have no idea if they are an asset to the company or a liability, how much money they make for the company, or what their value to the company is. The mentality is, "I must be doing something right, because they haven't fired me yet!" The bad part of this thinking is that technicians may be making the company enough money to receive wage increases, and not ever know it because they have no idea what their "value" is to the company. The other side of this is that technicians may be receiving more money than they deserve, which deprives the company and other technicians from receiving the money they deserve. If a technician is a liability (an employee who is costing the company money), the money the company is losing has to come from the company. This restricts the company from growing and also takes away wage increases for other employees because there is not as much money available as there could be.

I recommend technicians analyze their performance on a yearly basis. The reason I prefer a yearly review instead of monthly reviews is that the yearly reviews will even out the peaks and valleys that come with

1

working in the HVAC/R industry. The busy times will balance out the slow times and give technicians an accurate account of what their value is.

Every time I am involved in these evaluations I find they are not accurate. Everyone feels they are worth more money than they are receiving. Their thought is that they make so much money for the company that they should be getting paid a great deal of money more than they are. Technicians have not been exposed to and really do not understand the costs of doing business. They see all the money coming in, but have no idea of the amount of money that is needed to operate a company.

Another reason I hear from technicians wanting more money is, "I bust my butt for this company!" Though it may be true, it is no proof that more money is deserved. Should you get a raise while you are busting your butt on several call-backs? Technicians have to understand it is their responsibility to consistently perform at a level beyond their pay. This will ensure that their value to the company will always exceed what is expected, which means the technicians' pay should constantly be raised to equal their value. To give you an example, when athletes have a great year, their value to their team is extremely high; the athlete gets rewarded with a new contract with an extremely high pay increase. The next year, the same athlete has an average year and everyone wants to run the athlete out of town because the athlete's value to the team has dropped. Your boss fears the same result.

Wage increases are always given, never taken away. If a technician has a bad year, the company does not take money away from the technician. Part of the responsibility of accepting a wage increase is to continually increase your value to the company. Ask yourself this question before requesting a pay increase: "Where is the extra money for my raise going to come from?" It is not going to come from the owner's personal bank account. It has to come from the company's bank account, which means it has to come from you, because the money you bring in is deposited to the company's bank account. Technicians need to justify that the amount of money they bring into the company supports their need for a wage increase. We work for money! A business needs to make money! You probably hear discussions about the importance of customer service, consumer relations, improving your attitude, etc. These are all "soft skills" for which companies pay money to train their technicians to make more money. If technicians have a negative attitude towards the company, their value to the company is not as much as it could be; hence their wage is not what it could be. A negative attitude will be reflected in the amount of money a technician will make for the company because customers will notice it and not feel comfortable spending money with the company.

The question is, "How do I determine what my value is to the company?" Technicians need to know these three factors to determine what their value to the company is and whether or not they deserve a wage increase:

INVOICE TOTALS FOR THE YEAR

The amount of money, adding all invoice totals, you have billed for the company in a one-year period. This is total sales. Parts, labor, etc. Basically, every dollar you have made for the company. If you have no idea how much you bring in a year, you have no idea how much you are worth. Technicians always feel they bring in more money than they actually do. They remember the high-dollar jobs, but forget about vacations, doctor appointments, callbacks, and personal time off. These may be necessary, but they do take away from your yearly invoice total. A technician who has yearly invoice sales of $50,000 cannot be paid $50,000 a year. The company needs a portion of the invoice total to pay for business expenses (material, service trucks, gas, insurance, technicians' vacation pay, etc.) and make a profit. The technician's wage also has to be taken from the invoice totals, so you should see the importance of knowing what your invoice totals for the year are. You and your boss, when discussing a pay raise, must know the yearly invoice total to accurately calculate your value to the company. It will be applied to a formula using two other factors, not only to determine your value to the company, but also to show you what you could be paid per hour that would still allow you to be considered an asset to the company.

SALES PER HOUR

Sales per hour is used in the formula with the invoice sales total, but this number is going to show how much money a technician brings into the company on average per hour. Sales per hour is the average amount of money, including parts, labor, service agreements, etc., that you have sold for the company per hour. This number is achieved by dividing your invoice totals for the year by the number of hours you have been paid by the company for the year. If your invoice totals for the year are $80,000 and you were paid for 2200 hours for the year, your sales per hour will be $36.36. This means that you have brought in $36.36 every hour you have been paid to work. It gives your value to the company in the same time frame as you get paid, by the hour. Basically, it is the amount of money you have made for the company per hour. The sales per hour is an important number because the formula is going to base what you should be paid on this number. You can receive a fixed portion of the sales per hour and still be an asset for the company. If your sales per hour is $36.36, this doesn't mean you should get paid $36.36 per hour. If that were the case, the company would not have any money for cost-of-doing-business expenses and would soon have to close the doors.

Here is an example on how this works. Let's say a technician brought in $100,000 in yearly invoice totals and was paid by the company for 2000 hours of work that year. The technician's sales per hour would be $50.00. Another technician brought in $50,000 in yearly invoice totals, but was only paid by the company for 1000 hours of work. This technician's sales per hour is also $50.00. These two technicians, not taking in account callbacks, could be paid the same hourly rate and be assets to the company. It is not as simple as saying, "I bring in more money so I should get paid more!" Invoice totals for the year alone are not enough information to evaluate a technician's value. But, when it is used in a formula to find sales per hour, a technician's value to a company can be found. The formula recognizes the money brought in by a technician, but it also takes into consideration the cost to the company to make the money.

CALLBACK RATIO IN PERCENT

The callback ratio is the percentage of callbacks a technician has, compared with the number of calls performed. For instance, if a technician has worked 100 service calls and 3 were callbacks, the callback ratio will be 3 percent. The callback ratio percentage shows the technician's competency in the field. A higher callback ratio means the technician has performed a lot of "free" work and probably needs more training before his value to the company will support a pay increase. Callbacks are things that happen; we all know that. But they do cost the company money. If the company spends a lot of money on callbacks, there is less money for pay increases. A good, quality technician should have a callback ratio under 4 percent. Anything above that will reduce the technician's value to the company.

It should not be difficult to obtain these numbers from an accountant, bookkeeper, or controller. Calculating the numbers yourself is not recommended, because it adds extra paperwork to your job every day and you should not get paid for it. Once you know your sales per hour, you can estimate how much money you should make by multiplying it by 0.28. In other words, with a callback ratio below 4 percent, you are worth

28 percent of your average sales per hour. If you have a high callback ratio, such as 8 percent, you are worth basically whatever the company thinks you are worth. If your sales per hour is $75.00, and you have a 3 percent callback ratio, you can and should be paid $21.00 per hour with the company maintaining a good profit margin.

Once you have made the decision that you do deserve a raise and can support your decision with facts, you have a couple of "approach" options. The first option is to have your boss compare your numbers to those of your coworkers who make more money than you. This is rolling the dice and more than likely will cause tension in the workplace. I recommend not using this method. A work environment filled with tension is not worth any amount of money. You will find out the importance of accomplishing goals as a team later. It is not recommended that you sneak fellow employees' numbers to validate your raise. Technicians assume their numbers are better. If they are, you have a valid point. If they are not, you will be denied a raise. Some people do not like this approach, but it is an accurate measuring stick and the competition will force technicians to improve their skills to keep up with the other technicians. The other option is to focus on your numbers and convince your boss that your numbers are sufficient enough to deserve more money. This may be difficult to do, depending on how strong your numbers are. This formula is very direct, with little room for argument. If it shows you should make $21.00 per hour, that is what you should make. The company will still make a reasonable profit, and the technicians will make a wage equal to their value.

It is very important to ask for a raise during the busy seasons. Your boss will not be able to deny you a raise based on a slowdown. Also, do not threaten to quit. When you look at the technicians in this industry who are making the most money, it is not the people who have ten years' experience. The people who are making the most money are the people who have ten years with one company, have great sales per hour, and have a low callback ratio. I do not recommend changing companies for money. Technicians have to prove their abilities, learn a new employee manual, and establish a new customer base, and very rarely does a move for more money satisfy both parties. Company loyalty is invaluable. With that being said, if your numbers show you are being paid well under what you should be, and you are refused a pay increase, you have the right to search for other employment opportunities and I recommend that you do.

It may sound as if I am dancing with words, but I have had a few owners, not many but a few, tell me, "There is no technician worth twenty dollars per hour." I, personally, would not work for one of these owners. If you are being paid $15.00 per hour, and the equation shows that you should be paid $20.00 per hour, you are losing $5.00 per hour. That is equal to roughly $11,000.00 per year. If you continue to work for that company for ten years, you will have lost $110,000.00 that could have been paid to you. You will have to use your own judgment to determine what is best for you. A lot of people do not mind accepting less money to work for a particular company; I am not one of them. I do believe in company loyalty, but I need that loyalty to be returned to me. Pay me what I am worth, and I promise you that I will work for you until I retire.

The highest-paid technician will have very positive yearly invoice totals, very good sales per hour, and a low callback ratio, along with a number of years with the same company. How many technicians do you know who have returned to a company after quitting? These technicians will soon leave the company again and the company will not want to rehire them again. Sooner or later, the word gets out about these technicians and every other company becomes hesitant about hiring them. These technicians will eventually be forced to accept a lower wage to work. If you are getting paid what the formula shows you should, I would definitely think twice about leaving the company for more money.

Here is the wage formula in an equation:

Yearly invoice totals divided by hours worked/year = average sales/hour
Average sales/hour x 28 percent = technician's hourly wage

The company needs a minimum of 72 percent of your sales/ hour to be profitable!

Here is an example of how the formula applies the numbers we talked about. Technician A is paid $15.00 per hour. The technician's yearly invoice total is $100,000 per year, with 2200 hours worked and an 8 percent callback ratio. The technician's sales per hour is $45.45 ($100,000 divided by 2200 hours). The technician is receiving 33 percent of the sales per hour (sales per hour of $45.45 divided by hourly wage of $15.00). Remember, once you figure out your numbers, look at them through the eyes of your boss. If the technician is receiving 33 percent of all sales, the company is left with 67 percent of the sales per hour, in this case, $30.45. Out of that $30.45, the company has to pay for the job materials, gas, vehicle maintenance, any benefits the technician receives (medical, retirement, dental, etc.), overhead, dispatcher, office personnel, phone bill, advertising, and any other expense that occurs with business. Plus, the technician worked 2200 hours for the year; if the average call was 4 hours, the technician performed (2200 hours divided by 4) 550 calls for the year. With an 8 percent callback ratio, the technician had to go back on 44 calls, received their wage, and was not able to invoice any money. The technician was paid (44 calls times 4 hours average per call) for 176 callback hours that the company could not collect on: 176 hours times $15.00 per hour, $2640 was paid to the technician for the years callbacks. This technician has to realize that a raise is not applicable. The yearly invoice total must be higher and the callback ratio must be lower. I would suggest concentrating on these two numbers before asking for a raise.

Technician B is paid $15.00 per hour. Imagine that this technician's yearly invoice total is $150,000 per year, with 2200 hours worked and a 2 percent callback ratio. The technician's sales per hour is $68.18 ($150,000 divided by 2200). This technician is receiving 22 percent of the sales per hour. Do the math and you will see Technician B getting paid $660 for the year's callbacks. Once again, look through the eyes of your boss. Technician A is not bringing in as much money, has more callbacks, but is receiving a larger percentage of the pie than Technician B. The numbers prove that Technician B does qualify for a raise. At a wage rate of 28 percent of the sales per hour, with a low callback rate, the company will be profitable and the technician will be paid accurately. Anything higher than 28 percent of the sales per hour is costing the company money. By using the 28 percent of sales per hour formula, Technician A should be paid what the company thinks he/she is worth (which I assure you, will be well under $15.00 per hour) and Technician B should be paid $19.09 per hour. Technicians have to average $577.00 of total invoice sales a day to reach $150,000 for the year. That goal can easily be achieved with the methods presented later in this book.

Now, I know this formula will not work for installers, service managers, and salesman. Keep in mind that I am a service technician, I educate service technicians, and this book is for service technicians.

CHAPTER 2
SOLVING THE PROBLEM

The best part of this book is that the information contained in it works no matter where you are located, whether you charge by the hour or charge flat-rate. If you are a technician who chooses to live in a big city, your invoice total per year will be higher due to the fact that your company should charge more, which means you should be paid more. If a technician chooses to live in a smaller town, the wages will not be as high because the company will probably charge less, decreasing the invoice totals for the year. Using the formula, technicians who work in Los Angeles will be paid considerably more than the technicians who work in Minnesota. That is the way it should be!

We have already covered, in Chapter 1, how to calculate what a technician should earn for a wage. If you have applied the formula, you will probably find that you are close to earning what you should. So now the question is, "How can I earn more?" The answer is simple. Increase your sales per hour and reduce your callback ratio. What does this mean? As in any other business, the more money you bring in, the more valuable you will be to the company. You, as a technician, have to put yourself in the position where the company will lose money if they lose you. You reach that position by bringing in an extraordinary amount of money. When a service technician who brings $50,000 in total invoice sales per year asks for a raise, the owner's first thought is, "Is this service technician worth it?" When a service technician who brings $150,000 in total invoice sales per year asks for a raise, the owner's first thought is, "Do I want to lose $150,000 in sales a year?" Which technician would you rather be?

After studying the methods in this book, you will see that an extra ten minutes at each call can increase your invoice totals for the year to such a level that your company cannot afford to lose you. You will be in the position to confidently ask for a raise and receive it.

The problem with stressing the importance of increasing yearly invoice totals is that technicians may try to sell customers equipment, parts, or services they do not need. Do not sell customers items they do not need to increase your invoice totals. Be professional. Attempting to sell customers items they do not need will result in their not calling your company again. They will call your competitor, increasing your competitor's invoice totals, and decreasing yours because they did not call you. Customers can sense when they are being taken advantage of. Our industry has been criticized for years because of this. Customers have access to information they have never have had before. They see the shows on television that expose technicians taking advantage of customers. Treat them as if there is a hidden camera on you. Be honest. You can increase your invoice totals honestly; you do not have to resort to taking advantage of the customer.

As far as lowering your callback ratio, you will have to determine the problem there. It can be only one of two problems. You need more training or you need more time on the call. These are the only two issues it may be. Usually, the high callback ratios come from technicians who have been in the industry less than three years. My advice to you is to be patient and attend every seminar you can. You are no different from anyone else in this profession. We have all been through training seminars and they have made us all better service technicians.

I was talking to a coworker of mine not too long ago who has been in the field for two years. He made the comment that when he is on call, his goal is not necessarily to fix the problem, but just to "get them up and going." He was referring to a grocery-store rack system which, to no fault of his, he was not comfortable working on. I asked him at what point in his career he planned on actually repairing the problem and not just "getting them up and going." He did not answer me. Our industry does a wonderful job of educating service technicians, but most service technicians do not take advantage of it. There are many organizations that meet once a month to offer service technicians continuing education. Here's the catch: You have to join them. If you are looking for an organization in your area, call me. I will get you in touch with one. Also, our industry supplies us with many HVAC/R magazines, self-study courses, informational literature, and seminars. To be a top service technician, you have to take advantage of these to stay current. Most technicians do not see the need for these, but they will eventually find out how valuable they are. I have heard all the excuses. *I need to spend time with my family. I had a previous engagement. My car broke down.* The list goes on and on. That is why some technicians are just getting equipment "up and going." And that is why their pay is low. They find the need for more education wasteful.

CERTIFICATION

In our industry there is a big push for certification. I support national certification, and believe it should have been a standard in our industry years ago. Just because you wear a uniform with a company name on it and drive a van with HVAC/R decals on it, does that mean you are qualified to repair the equipment? HVAC/R service technicians with less than two years of experience should take the ICE exams or equivalent and service technicians with more than three years should take the NATE exam or equivalent. Increase your value to the company by wearing a patch that shows the customer you have had the education and training to successfully pass a national certification test which qualifies you to repair their equipment. Some companies, along with their employees, have the attitude of "Certification will do nothing for us and is a waste of time and money." I will tell you this! I am the "type" of technician who uses the patches on my shoulders to put extra value into my sales and services, taking money away from the noncertified technician. I use my certifications to install extra value in my sale to separate myself from my competitors—and to increase my yearly invoice totals.

A customer—and this is a proven fact—is more willing to spend money with a technician who meets the industry standards than with a technician who feels the standards are a waste of time. If you are not certified (not the EPA Certification, because everyone is required to have that), you are losing money because you are losing opportunities. Certified technicians are taking advantage of your "don't need certification" attitude.

If your attitude is that certification is not worth receiving, it is I and thousands of other technicians like me, who are decreasing your yearly invoice totals, which results in decreasing your hourly pay rate. I inform the customers of my accomplishments. I inform them of the advantages of buying services from a certified technician. There are a lot of technicians who are not certified who are excellent service technicians, and I take advantage of their lack of certification to increase my total invoice totals, which decreases their yearly invoice totals. Here is my approach to the customer when informing them of my certification: "I realize the prices I quoted you for the repairs (or installation) of your equipment may be a little more than some of the other quotes you have received. But please allow me to ease your mind about the repair (or installation). I have, through training and experience, obtained industry certification [pointing to my patches], which proves I have the ability to supply you with the quality of service recommended by our industry." The customers will shift their focus from the price to the quality of service. Here is what they think. "I did not see patches on the other technicians who gave me a quote. I wonder if they are qualified?" The price becomes secondary. I get the job! I increase my yearly invoice totals! If you missed it, notice that I never refer to our industry as a trade. It is a profession. And I am a professional. Look at other professions. Doctors, lawyers, accountants—they are all required to attend seminars and complete certifications. You want to get closer to their pay, figure it out. It is up to you, no one else.

MORE THAN MONEY

Being an educator in the HVAC/R industry, I see how damaging the pay issue is to new recruits. Most people at the age of seventeen or eighteen do not know what they want to do for a living. At our school, we have informational days, where prospective students come to our school to research the programs we offer. The first question that is asked is, "How much money will I make when I graduate?" Well, in Minnesota, where I am, the starting wage is $11.00-$12.00 per hour. When the prospective students hear that number, I have lost their interest. They do not want to hear about any other benefits or rewards that come with our profession. They head off to the computer course that pays them $20.00 per hour when they graduate. Our program has close to sixty inquiries a year from students interested in HVAC/R; we educate roughly fifteen of them.

I have mentioned the other rewards and benefits. I will tell you an incident that happened to me that the computer people will never have happen to them and money will never buy. I was called out at 11:00 P.M. on a rural no-heat call. The temperature was minus-20 degrees and the wind was blowing pretty strongly. In these conditions, it doesn't take long to notice your furnace is out. As the dad walks me through the house, I see the mother with their two children, about five and seven years of age, huddled on the couch under a blanket, trying to stay warm. The house is at 55 degrees and dropping. I get escorted to the basement to find the igniter defective on an L.P. gas high-efficient furnace. I replace the igniter, check the operation of the furnace, make a few recommendations about what I feel should be done the next day, and start to do the paperwork. I was there for about an hour, so the house was starting to warm up. As I was walking back through the house with my toolbox, I saw the look in the kids' eyes. I could tell by their look that, they thought I was some sort of superhero. They were just amazed that their house was too cold to sleep in before I got there, and warm when I left. I imagined them thinking, "*Why would someone leave their warm house in the middle of a cold night to come and make sure our house was warm?*" The parents thanked me

11

and paid me, but it was not worth as much as what the children did for me. This is why I do what I do! This is why I am in the HVAC/R industry.

People need me. People need my knowledge, skills, and abilities. You will not realize how important you are to people until something like that happens to you. Sure, every day you are needed to repair something, but to have people (in my case, the two children) who have no idea what you are about, think you're a superhero because you did your job, is worth more than any amount of money they could have paid me.

Some companies go out of their way to show their technicians appreciation, but it is not the same. Technicians will always debate if it is truly a compliment of their ability or a motivational statement to keep the technicians loyal to the company. It seems as soon as you get a compliment from the boss, you find out other technicians had the same conversation. Take the compliments however you want, but you really won't know your value until someone who has nothing to gain from your services recognizes you for your abilities. You will know when you have had one of these experiences, because you feel like you are on top of the world. You get excited and will never want to leave the industry. You will just want to make more money.

SERVICES

Increasing your pay! So far I have explained in great detail that in order to increase your pay, you must increase your value to the company by raising your yearly invoice totals. Here is one of the ways this can be accomplished.

Before I explain it to you, I would like to have you first write down on a piece of paper three reasons a customer should buy from your company instead of your competitor. Do not focus your answers on what you believe to be a negative quality of your competitor (for instance, "Don't buy from Joe because...."), but rather list the positive qualities of your company (for instance, "A customer would want to buy from our company because we offer...."). You will have a hard time convincing a customer to buy anything from you by talking bad about your competitors, plus, if you talk bad about a competitor, more than likely they will return the favor. So, please take the time to write down three reasons why a customer should buy from your company.

Now, look at your answers and read them back to yourself. If any of your answers have the word "quality" or its equal (such as "fix it right the first time"), please cross them off. If any of your answers have the word "warranty," please cross them off. If any of your answers have the word "reputation" or its equal (such as "been in business for twenty years"), cross them off. If any of your answers have the phrase "customer service" or its equal (such as "we don't leave a mess" or "fast service"), cross them off. If any of your answers have the phrase "emergency service," cross them off. How many do you have left? Here is the point! HVAC/R companies sell two things: HVAC/R equipment and HVAC/R service. All companies are selling the same equipment. In most customers' minds, a 10 SEER 3-ton A/C is a 10 SEER 3-ton A/C. It does not matter who makes it as long as it cools their house and it has a five-year warranty. Every manufacturer has had a problem with their equipment at some point and most HVAC/R technicians are aware of these problems. You do not have any advantage over your competitor by focusing on and stressing the brand name of your equipment, because the customer does not care who made it and the brand you sell has had some problems at one time. It may have been twenty years ago, but your competitor is probably using this selling technique: "They have had some problems with their equipment." The best way to separate our company from our competitors is to stress to the customer what services our company can provide for them. Here's the problem! We end up selling the same services.

As the exercise above shows, if you have any of your three answers crossed off, you are selling the same services as your competitor. "Our company has been in business for twenty-five years, the equipment comes with a five-year warranty, we clean up when we are done, and if you have a problem any time of the day or night with the equipment, we will be available to repair it." These are very strong selling points, but your competitor is selling the same **services**. We are forcing our customers to focus on the price to determine who gets the job. Same equipment! Same services! $300 difference on price! It doesn't take a genius to figure out which company will get the sale. You have lost the sale, which means you have lost money on your yearly invoice total, which means you have lost an opportunity to increase your wage.

You need to take advantage of what your company does have and also the training the company supplies the technicians. It is fine to use the services listed above in your sale, but you need to add more to show the customer it is best for them to spend more money with your company. "We may be $300 higher on the price, but along with all the services we have talked about, I feel I need to add that all of our technicians have been factory-trained to repair our equipment, have the education and knowledge to pass a national HVAC/R certification [pointing to the patches on my arm, which more than likely, my competitor does not have. See above], we inventory most of the replacement parts for our equipment in our trucks, and we would be more than happy to set up an appointment to meet you in our showroom so you can actually see and hear our equipment in operation." Just as we need to add more value to get paid more, we need to add more "service" value to our company to overcome a price difference.

Some customers base their purchase on price. No matter what you do, they will choose the least expensive bid. But, you will find by adding "service" value to your technique, it is not as many as you may think. "We were $300 too high on this bid!" This bid was not lost because you charged $300 too much. This bid was lost because you tried to sell the same equipment and same services as another company that was $300 less. You forced your customer to select the lowest bid because there was no reason to pay your company more money. To increase your year invoice totals, you need to sell these jobs.

Create a sheet of twenty reasons a customer should buy from your company, laminate it, and carry it in your truck so you have the reasons available for review before you quote a job to the customer. You will soon memorize them and know which of the twenty get the most positive results from the customers. You will develop the habit of adding "service" value to your bid, which will overcome a price difference, which will sell more jobs, which will add more money to your yearly invoice totals, which will increase your value to the company, which will increase your wage. Most importantly, we are not taking advantage of our customers. We are informing them that the extra money spent with our company is a good investment, because we will take care of them as best we can, keep them comfortable, and eventually save them money.

I begin teaching this method to our students the first day of class. I ask them to write down on paper four reasons why a company would want to hire them. The answers I get are: dependable, good with tools, hard-working, and good with people. All of the students are offering companies the same qualities. After I read the answers back to them, they all laugh and see the problem. I explain to them that they are going to be competing for jobs not only with their classmates, but with every other graduate in the state. And in order to succeed in acquiring employment, they will have to work hard and develop unique qualities that will bene-fit companies. Their first assignment is to create twenty reasons why a company would want to hire them. Throughout the next two-years they are at our school, we (the students and I) continually review them and adjust them to assure they are accurate and powerful. Our students have an edge in the interview process because they are prepared. They know the qualities they possess that separate them from other interviewers. And they use their qualities to obtain employment. As shown, technicians can use this same method to obtain and retain customers. This method adds value to our students in the employer's mind, and it will add value to you and your company in the customer's mind.

KNOW YOUR PRODUCT

Earlier, I had told you that a 3-ton 10 SEER air conditioner is a 3-ton 10 SEER air conditioner. Most customers do not care who makes the product as long as it does the job. But technicians have to be knowledgeable about the products they sell. For instance, how much estimated money will a customer save by purchasing a 12 SEER instead of a 10 SEER? A 12 SEER is initially more money than a 10 SEER, which will increase your yearly invoice totals, but will save the customer money every month in operating costs. If a technician has no idea how to estimate the monthly savings, the customer will certainly choose the less-expensive 10 SEER. Customers do not mind spending money up front as long as there is a payback. Technicians must have knowledge about the products they sell, to convince the customer that the least expensive choice is not always the least expensive choice—it will eventually cost them more money.

Here's a good example of technicians not knowing about a product: a programmable thermostat. They inform the customer how great the thermostat is, how decorative it is, how "everyone" is buying it, and how they install so many of them that they have a difficult time keeping the thermostat in stock. They make the sale, wire it, and begin to program it **USING THE BOOK**. Your customer is thinking, "You sell so many programmable thermostats that you need the instruction manual to install it!" They will doubt not only your abilities, but also your honesty.

Know about your products, know how to install them, and know the benefits to the consumer before you offer the product. Do not familiarize yourself about the products at the cost of your customers. They will feel as if they are being overcharged, because it takes longer to install a product using the installation manual. This will result in reducing the value of the sale. Read installation manuals the day or the night before you do the job. Know the clearances of the furnace before you get to the job. Know how many long-radius elbows can be used on the high-efficient furnace vent before you get to the job. Know the size of the refrigerant line connections on the condensing unit and the evaporator before you get to the job. Know how to program the thermostat before you get to the job. Knowing about your products will prevent "wasted" trips to the wholesaler, keep your customer satisfied, and increase your value to the company.

With all of the new technology that is out, I realize the amount of time it takes to keep up with the changing of products. Technicians could spend all of their off-time reading installation manuals. This is why I like to subscribe to all of the industry magazines that I can. The magazines do not get as detailed as the installation manuals, but I gain enough information about the product, from people who have already used it, to decide if the product is something I should offer or not. Magazines inform me of all the new products that are available. I cannot offer our customers an item if I do not know it exists. Sometimes I find out about certain products before the wholesalers do. I will call to get information on a certain item and they have no idea what I am talking about. It is my responsibility to my customers to offer them as many options as I can and if I am not knowledgeable about new products, I will not be able to serve them at the level they deserve.

Quite few years ago, I was the last of five contractors to give an estimate to replace a boiler in a fairly historic, rural house. The owner wanted to update the heat source, but keep the existing original cast-iron radiators in each room. As I entered the basement (where the boiler was located), here is what I observed. The boiler was an old boiler that, for some reason, had been converted from fuel oil to propane. The heating system was not zoned, which resulted in wide temperature differences between rooms. And, most unusual, there was a fuel-oil water heater next to the converted propane boiler. The customer had to contact two separate businesses, one for fuel oil and one for propane, to accommodate his heating and domestic hot water needs. After listening to what he had in mind, I asked him, "Do you find it to be an inconvenience to have two separate fuels operating your boiler and water heater?" I knew what the answer would be before I asked the question, but this was an opportunity for me to explain my ideas to him. I asked him, "If you could choose one fuel, which fuel would you prefer to use, fuel oil or propane?" His response was propane, because it was cleaner and less expensive to maintain the burners than fuel oil. Here was my idea (I must inform you, this was at a time when all fuels were expensive.): Replace the boiler with an 86 percent efficient propane boiler. Install zone valves and repipe the system to accommodate four zone valves to eliminate the temperature swings between rooms. Supply and install an indirect water heater and pipe it as zone 5 off of the boiler manifolds, and remove the existing fuel-oil water heater. Because of the high fuel rates, supply and install an electric boiler in series with the new propane boiler and electrically connect it to an off-peak panel to get the reduced kilowatt rate from the power company. I explained the benefits of each part of the system to him, delivered a proposal with the cost of each segment of the job (in case he does not want the complete job, he may at least want me to change the boiler), invited him to call if he had any other questions, and appreciated the opportunity he had given me to bid on his project.

The next day, at the local wholesalers', I was talking to one of the other contractors who was called to give this customer an estimate. He informed me of his bid amount and wanted to know what I quoted. I told him I was $1100.00 higher, and asked him what was included in his bid. He told me he had quoted a propane boiler, system zoning, standard propane water heater, and an electric boiler connected to an off-peak electrical panel. He smiled and joked to the wholesaler that they should order the equipment for the job, because he was sure he was going to be doing the work. "What was in your bid?" he asked.

"Pretty much the same, but I quoted an indirect water heater." I replied.

"An indirect water heater?" he asked.

I said, "Yeah! With our climate, an indirect water heater is the way to go, because the boiler is going to maintain 180-degree water for six to seven months out of the year."

"Sounds expensive! What does the boiler water temperature have to do with domestic hot water?" he asked.

Now I knew the problem. He obviously had no idea what an indirect water heater was and had no idea how to install one. I explained the whole operation of the indirect water heater to him and advised him that he had better get some training on them.

I did get approval from the customer to do the job, because of the value in my services and the knowledge I had of the equipment I was offering. The other three contractors quoted just the boiler replacement, so my quote was the highest of all the quotes. Our company was selected to perform the job for the customer because we were going to save him money in the long run and I was able to answer his questions about the equipment. It was the indirect water heater that sold this job! The indirect water heater was the item that separated our company from the others. It wasn't the price. The customer did not mind spending more money now, because he was going to save more money in the future. Plus, it increased my yearly invoice total. By knowing the advantages and benefits of the equipment I offer, I can be the highest-priced quote and still have the customer accept the bid. It's not about being the lowest bid. It's about your customer's justifying the additional cost. Not only do you have to know about equipment, but you also need to know about any parts that you sell (see the programmable thermostat example above). If you stock a part in your service van and you have no idea what it is for or how it is installed, take it home and read the instructions. I am sure that if you ask, your company will not mind.

CHAPTER 3
ATTITUDE

There are four types of attitudes displayed by service technicians. I want to begin by discussing two of these attitudes that are very similar. One is positive and is definitely needed to increase your pay. Confidence! One is negative, will cost you money, and will destroy your career before you know it. Arrogance! The day you think you know everything about this industry is the day you go from confident to arrogant. I have been in HVAC/R for eighteen years and still learn a lot every day. I have a confident attitude about my abilities, but realize that learning will be endless. I learn from people who are just entering the industry and people who have been affiliated with it for longer than I have. I learn from customers and other technicians. I am continually reading trade magazines, keeping up to date with new products, and continually reviewing local and national guidelines.

Confidence allows you to feel good about yourself. It allows your customers to feel secure that the work will be done properly. It is an attitude that follows you. It can spread to coworkers. People can sense you have the ability to service their needs before you do anything. It's knowing that whatever the customer's problem will be, I can repair it. Confidence in your ability will make your job easier. A technician is able to better communicate with the customer because of it. When describing a problem or a repair, there is no stuttering or hesitation. "Mr. Jones, your condenser was full of dirt and debris, restricting the air flow through it, which caused your compressor to overheat and burn out." Everything flows nicely with confidence.

Confidence can be developed. All personalities have the ability to show confidence. People who feel they cannot perform the task have no confidence. If you were the customer, would you prefer to pay someone who is confident or someone who is hesitant and indecisive? And that is the purpose of this book: taking advantage of every opportunity to increase your hourly wage. To increase your hourly wage you have to increase your yearly invoice totals. As you have already read, there are honest ways of doing this that do not take advantage of the customers.

For customers, seeing a confident service technician creates ease; it allows them to relax. Seeing an arrogant service technician causes tension and changes the customers' focus from getting the equipment repaired to getting the technician out of their house. Arrogance will destroy your career, no matter what it is, faster than anything else. It sends the message that you know everything there is to know about HVAC/R. Your way is the only way. This prevents you from listening to your customers, and finding out what their ideas are. Arrogance makes your customer feel uncomfortable, and uncomfortable customers will not buy from you. If they do not buy from you, your yearly invoice totals are lower than what they should be, which makes your hourly wage lower. More importantly, arrogance prevents technicians from continually learning. They don't have to learn anymore, they know it all. Have you ever wondered who is the best HVAC/R service technician in the world? It changes daily, but I would wager all the technicians in the running are confident and continue their education. And I would also wager they do not feel underpaid. They don't have to.

As there is a fine line between confidence and arrogance, the other two attitudes are as different as day and night. You may have both types at the place you are employed. The first one is a go-getter! This type of service technician loves to go to work, enjoys being in a service truck, enjoys meeting different people every day, and would never make it in the "office" world. These technicians do not mind climbing on a roof whether it is 10 degrees or 110 degrees. These service technicians do not mind pulling call, taking a service call at 4:30 or occasionally showing up for work a couple of hours early. These service technicians usually are the first one to work every morning, preparing for the day's work. They love "industry" talk and cannot seem to get enough of it. They can rattle off a part number as if it were their phone number. Go to their houses and you will find industry-related magazines on their coffee tables. They never miss a seminar or educational event. They are great technicians, who usually get promoted in a very short amount of time.

The last attitude is just the opposite. These service technicians feel they are being taken advantage of. No matter what the company does to try and satisfy them, it is not enough. These technicians are continuously late, do not attend any company functions, and usually do not associate with anyone they work with. These technicians do not continue their education, does not try to improve themselves professionally, and seem to be content just to complain about their jobs. It takes people, including customers, a very short time to identify this technician.

I took one of our students to a company in Sioux Falls, South Dakota, for a job interview. To get to the interview office, we had to walk through the warehouse. While we were walking through the warehouse, we heard a technician say, "This f——— place!" as he was rummaging through a large cardboard box, looking for a certain part. The student looked at me and expressed, "What are we doing here?" This service technician had seen us walk in and knew we were there. Here is the problem with this. Customers have to walk through the warehouse to get to the showroom. We could have been customers wanting to spend money with this company. That one phrase out of that technician's mouth convinced our student this was not the place where he would want to work. It would also have convinced a customer not to spend money there.

If you are a technician with this attitude, you have two options to increase your pay. One is to become more positive towards the profession and improve your skills. Attitude is a factor when a pay increase is discussed. Show the company you support it and you want to be a team player to achieve certain business goals. Face the facts: You are not going to get rich until your boss does. Option 2 is to change your career to something you enjoy. Now, I have to inform you that if you have a negative attitude, you will probably carry it over to a different career. You will find something to complain about no matter what field you are in. I recommend Option 1, but give it time. You cannot change your attitude overnight, which means you will not increase your pay overnight.

This all goes to presenting yourself to the customers in a professional manner. We want them to buy from us and we want them to call us again. We want customers to buy from us and continue to use our services. We do not want them to spend their money with our competitors; we want it. So we have to be better, more professional, offer more services, and be more confident. You will find customers are not afraid to spend money, as long as they feel there is value. They are buying new vehicles for $50,000. Why? Because they see the value in buying a new vehicle. The technicians' attitude, confidence, and professionalism can bring added value, and that added value can be the deciding factor in whether the customer buys from you or your competitor. If the customer buys from your competitor, your competitor's yearly invoice sales total is increased and not yours. If you find a lot of customers do not buy from you because of price, check your approach. You did not convince them there was enough value. Don't complain to your boss that the prices are too high and the prices are affecting your sales. Think of what you could have done to improve your approach and add value. Then, experiment on your next customer. Individualism is required. Be yourself and find out what works for you, then stick with it. You will find the approach that works for you and see your sales per hour increase.

Not only will a positive attitude increase your value to the company by increasing your yearly sales total, but it will also increase your value to the company by setting an example for young technicians. You are a mentor, and what you teach other employees, whether by your attitude or your work ethic, has a lot to do with the company's success. A negative technician will display negative qualities, which will transfer to other technicians. Eventually, the entire company has a negative atmosphere. It is not a fun place to work and most important, it is not a fun place to shop. Customers can sense the tension when they enter the building. They will not spend money with the company. If you have a negative attitude, you might as well quit reading this book now, because nothing will increase your pay. It does not matter how many services your offer, how you approach your customers, or how technically skilled you are. Your attitude will lose the sale.

CHAPTER 4

THE SHELF TECHNIQUE

Welcome to the money page. Chapter 4 is going to be worth the price of the book by itself. Please pay close attention to this chapter because it explains what you can do to increase your yearly invoice totals, which increases your sales per hour.

How can you increase your pay? This is a question that is asked in every HVAC/R magazine that is printed. The answers vary from commissions to bonuses to rewarding technicians for no callbacks. Everyone involved seems to have the solution to the problem, but the next month, there the question is again in our industry magazines. Here is the real question. Can a technician whose invoices total $50,000 a year get paid $50,000 a year? The only way to increase a technician's income is to increase the technician's invoice totals. Here is the solution.

TECHNICIANS NEED TO BUILD A SHELF!

Technicians do not have a 20,000 square-foot building to display what they are offering. They operate out of a service truck, which has created the mentality of how our industry does business. Troubleshoot the equipment, fix the problem, be professional with the customer, collect the money, go to the next customer, and do it again. This way of operating a business is limiting technicians' pay because it is limiting their invoice totals. Technicians have to create a "shelf" and help the customer visualize what is on it.

Wal-Mart has huge buildings full of products on shelves. If you were looking for a light switch, you would find on one end of the shelf a generic light switch for $0.78 and on the other end of the shelf you would find a nice, decorative light switch for $5.98. Between these two light switches on the shelf, you will find many other light switches priced somewhere between $0.78 and $5.98. Each light switch has its advantages and disadvantages, depending on what the customer is looking for. The customers have to make a decision about which light switch is right for them.

Technicians have not been trained to create a "shelf" to present to the customer. This limits the customer's options, which limits the technician's sales, which limits a technician's pay. Creating a "shelf" is not difficult and requires only a sheet of paper, a pencil, and brochures.

For example, let's create a service call. The example will be billed in the hourly rate format using $40.00 an hour for simplicity in calculating, but it works just as well for a flat rate by adding the extra tasks. A condenser fan motor has failed because of bad bearings on a 2-ton central A/C, which is eleven years old. Using the old way of doing business, our invoice would look like this (Prices are just for the example):

Fan motor	$95.00
Capacitor	$ 8.00
Labor	$80.00
Total invoice	$183.00

On our invoice, we explain that the motor and capacitor come with a one-year factory warranty (or whatever it may be). We would collect $183.00 and go to the next call. **STOP!** There is the problem. The technician has limited the sale. The customer has no option but to replace the motor. The whole job took two hours so the sales per hour ($183.00 divided by 2 hours) is $91.75.

Instead of replacing the fan motor instantly, the technician can take ten minutes and create a "shelf" on a piece of paper to present to the customer. The "shelf" will contain Option 1, the $183.00 repair listed above, but will also include:

OPTION 2

Fan motor	$95.00
Capacitor	$ 8.00
Chemically flush condenser	$15.00
High-pressure safety control	$45.00
Low-pressure safety control	$45.00
New fan blade	$36.50
Labor	$120.00
Total Invoice	$364.50

As the technician presents this option, he explains the importance of a clean condenser and the need for the safety controls; the fan blade may be out of balance, causing the bad bearings in the motor. He also presents warranty information. Now, let's look at the sales per hour. This option took three hours so the sales per hour ($364.50 divided by three hours) are $121.50. The technician has increased the sales per hour by $29.75. Our "shelf" is not full yet!

OPTION 3

New lower-brand 10 SEER condensing unit installed $1300.00

This will take four hours. Sales per hour is $350.00

OPTION 4

New name-brand 10 SEER condensing unit installed $1600.00

This will take four hours. Sales per hour is $400.00

While presenting Options 3 and 4, technicians must be accurate in presenting the advantages of purchasing a new condensing unit, such as the warranty information of not only the manufacturer, but also the labor warranty of the company they work for. Also, the sales per hour should not be listed on your paper. It is listed here to show you the opportunities you are missing to increase your invoice totals.

There is still plenty of room on our "shelf." How about adding the options of a higher SEER condensing unit or a 410-A condensing unit? These require the sale of a new evaporator coil and new refrigeration lines. Take the time to explain the advantages of each option that is on your "shelf." Explain the importance of energy-efficient units and environmentally safe refrigerants to the customers. You are not selling them something they do not need; you are offering them options. Do not prefer one option to another. Let the customers decide what is best for them. They may choose the $183.00 repair, but they may choose to replace that old air conditioner. Some people say, "You are trying to sell them something they don't need!" I tell them, "I am not trying to sell them any certain item at all. I am giving them options to choose from. They will decide what to buy, if any. If I do not offer them options, I am controlling what is done to their equipment. A technician should not be able to make the repairs without consulting with the customer. Part of my job is to give them quotes of not only the least expensive repair, but also all repairs that will save them money in the future." I recommend listing the least-expensive repair as Option one, the second least expensive as Option 2, the third least expensive as Option three, and so on. When offered options, your customers will actually shop as if they are in a store. Using the option sheet above, here is what will happen: "Option 1 is $183.00 for the basic repair. For another $180.00, I can get the basic repair, pressure controls to protect the most expensive part of the system, the condenser flushed with chemicals, and a new fan blade with Option 2. But, for $900.00 more, I can get a brand new low-brand air conditioner with an excellent warranty in Option 3. And for another $300.00, I can get a top-of-the-line air conditioner with an excellent warranty in Option 4." They work their way up your option sheet and justify the added cost by using the first option as a baseline. They start with basic repair because they figure that is going to be the least amount of money they will spend, and subconsciously justify spending more as they move up through the options.

Let me show you how the shelf technique works with a service call. Our city, which is located on the border of Minnesota and North Dakota, had a severe storm one night. The winds reached 100 miles per hour with heavy rains and hail. The next day I was scheduled to install a condenser fan motor in a 7.5-ton Carrier rooftop unit on a mall. When I climbed on the roof, I saw that a 4-ton rooftop has been blown off its roof curb and slammed into another 4-ton rooftop on a different part of the mall. The first task I did was replacing the condenser fan motor I was scheduled to do. When I finished this task, I invoiced it out. I then called the mall owners to inform them of what I found and to get authorization to set the 4-ton rooftop back on its roof curb and also to inspect all nine rooftop units on the building. It will take four people to reset the rooftop and a half-hour per unit for the inspections. The quoted price for these tasks combined was $895.00. The quoted price was approved and I informed the owner that the inspection was just that, an inspection. Any repairs that would have to be made would be noted, quoted, and presented to him for authorization before the repairs would be made. We reset the rooftop on its curb and I started the inspections. The results of the inspection were severe. The high wind and hail had damaged the fins on all nine rooftop condensers beyond repair and destroyed the economizer filters. The rooftop that was off its curb was damaged beyond repair, as was the rooftop it had struck. At this time, I built my shelf with options for the customer. Remember, I had already made $895.00, plus the invoice for the initial condenser fan motor repair, for the day.

OPTION 1

(2) 4-ton rooftop condensing units with 125,000 btu natural gas heat and economizeR. Includes everything to install units but electrical **$7995.00**

(7) 4-ton condenser coils including installation, recovery, driers, evacuating, nitrogen, charging, and start-up **$10,500.00**

(14) economizer filters **$840.00**

TOTAL AMOUNT: $19,335.00

That is a really nice job, and most technicians would be content with this sale. But look at the other option I put on my shelf!

OPTION 2

(9) 4-ton rooftops with 125,000 btu natural gas heat and economizers. Price includes complete installation except for electrical. Compressors have a 5-year warranty and our company will supply a two-year parts and labor warranty on the new rooftops.

TOTAL AMOUNT: $27,360.00

Now, I have to explain some details here. The mall owner did receive quotes from our competitors. I do not know what their quotes were, but I can tell you there was only one person involved who went into the mall, bought a disposable camera for $6.00, took pictures of the damage, and informed the mall owner of the pictures on his quote. That technician is not only the technician whose quote was accepted, but is also the person who wrote this book. It doesn't take a genius to figure out this was going to be an insurance claim, and insurance companies love pictures. Another detail in our company's favor was that the units would fit right on the existing roof-curbs with no adaptions. Also, I called our supplier, informed them of the situation, and received a greatly reduced price on the units if I purchased nine of them. Take a look at Option 1: I quoted $7995.00 for two units. That is $3997.50 for each unit. In Option 2, I quoted $27,360.00 for nine units. That is $3040.00 for each unit.

Now, I want you to think about what has happened here. The insurance claim will cover Option 1. The mall owner is going to get an insurance check for $19,335.00 to repair the units. If the mall owners want to contribute $8025.00 of their own money, combined with the insurance coverage, they get nine new rooftop units. For $892.00 per unit, they get a new air conditioner, a new heater, a new economizer, a five-year compressor warranty, and a two-year parts and labor warranty from our company. They choose buying all new units. Let's figure my sales per hour.

In Option 1, each condenser was quoted for five hours and each rooftop was quoted for one hour. The total job was quoted for thirty-seven hours.

$19,335.00 divided by 37 hours = $523.00 sales per hour.

That is pretty good and most technicians would be happy with this, but look at what they would have missed if they did not offer Option 2. Each rooftop was quoted for one hour and remember, there were nine of them.

$27,360.00 divided by 9 hours = $3,040.00 sales per hour.

I have increased my sales per hour by almost **six** times. And here is the extra time I have in the job by presenting the options. Buying a camera and taking pictures: fifteen minutes; calling our supplier and getting a quote for nine rooftops: fifteen minutes; and writing Option 2 on a proposal: fifteen minutes. Do not forget that I had to call our supplier to get prices for the condenser coils and I had to write the proposal for Option 1 anyway. So for an extra forty-five minutes to offer my customer options, I increased my sales per hour by $2517.00. Higher sales per hour make you more valuable to your company. The more valuable you are, the more money you are worth.

It is very important to present your "shelf" on every service call. If a technician has a sales goal of $3000 a week and presents the "shelf" to all twenty customers for that week, the technician needs just 10 percent (two out of the twenty customers) to buy from the high end of the "shelf" to meet his sales goal. If the technician has the same sales goal of $3000 a week and presents the "shelf" to only five of the twenty customers that week, the technician now needs 40 percent (two out of five customers) to buy from the high-priced end of the shelf, reducing the chance of meeting the sales goal.

The more customers who choose to purchase the middle-to-high-priced items, the more your yearly invoice totals will increase. Remember, this is where the extra money to pay you is coming from. Wal-Mart does not take advantage of customers; they are offering them options. Service technicians need to apply the same business policies to increase their sales per hour.

The most important thing to remember is not to repair the problem right away. After you troubleshoot and find the source of the problem, build a "shelf" with as many options for your customer as you can. Then use common sense, such as taking pictures on an insurance claim, to add value to your sale. Take your "shelf" to the customers and let them decide between your options. Then perform the work of the option that they chose. The final decision on what has to be done is not yours!

By giving your customers a choice, you will find that they respect you as a technician. They are so used to the "old way" of doing business, that sometimes they stutter in disbelief that they have a choice. Be prepared! Have your truck stocked with brochures you can give them. Be sure to read the brochures before handing them out so you can answer any questions they have. Customers love visuals. They like to see what they are purchasing, and most of the time a brochure is the best we have. If you offer a lower-brand and a name-brand unit, leave both brochures with the customers. Let them read through it and decide which one is best for them. I like to hand the brochures to the customer when we are discussing the options. For instance, "Mrs. Jones, here's a piece of literature on the (lower-brand) air conditioner that is Option 3. It is not the top-of-the-line unit, but as you can see, it is a very attractive unit that comes with a really good warranty for the money. It is a little bit noisier than the (top of the line) unit, which is shown in this brochure and is Option 4 [I hand the customer the top of the line brochure]. The (top-of-the-line) unit, as noted on the brochure, is more durable and quieter, and comes with higher-quality components and an excellent warranty." Notice I am not pushing for her to choose either one. I am informing her of the advantages of both. I never say anything negative about any of the options, such as "I wouldn't buy this (lower-brand) unit, because we have been very disappointed with the units we have installed." This is pushing the customer to choose the top-of-the-line option. Don't do that! The customer may want a new air conditioner, but can afford only the lower-brand. You could lose the sale by pushing for the top-of-the-line brand. We do not want the customers to feel pressured in any way. Allow them to choose what they want. As long as they are comfortable and feel you can satisfy their needs, they will choose one of your options. Any option they choose will increase your yearly invoice totals.

If they choose none of your options, you did not use the right approach and left the customer questioning your ability to satisfy their needs or they were not seeing enough value for the price. Try a different approach on your next customer. Review the list of reasons why customers should buy from your company, offer a few more options, study your equipment brochures, make sure your option sheet is neat and legible, make sure you offer various finance options (covered in a later chapter), etc. Do not use excuses for losing a sale: "They weren't going to buy from us anyway." That "excuse" is also covered later in the book.

CHAPTER 5
THE INSURANCE TECHNIQUE

I f I were to offer you insurance against callbacks for $2.00 per service call, would you take it? Here is how it works: For every service call you do, you pay me $2.00. I guarantee, for that fee, that the repair you make on the equipment will not fail for the length of your company's labor warranty. Would you buy it? No matter how you answer, this method will benefit you.

I include this technique because it will not only increase your yearly invoice totals but will also reduce your callback ratio. It is a technique that forces technicians to perform a job thoroughly, while increasing their yearly invoice totals. How many times have you had a service call, and when you get there the evaporator is completely "froze up"? The first check all service technicians do is an inspection of the air filter. If it is plugged, the usual business practice is to replace it, defrost the coil, check suction pressure, and charge the minimum fee of $75.00. The technician is happy because the minimum fee covers more time than he spent there. Easy money! Two days later, the same call comes in again.

Here is the same service call using the insurance technique. (Prices are for example only.) I will put it in the format that I am presenting it to the customer, so you will comprehend how it works.

"Mrs. Jones, I have found that your evaporator coil inside the plenum [I would point to the plenum] is iced up, not allowing air to flow through it."

"This was probably caused by the air filter's not being replaced as often as necessary. [I show her the plugged air filter.] The air filter is designed to catch most particles that pass through it, to maintain clean air in your home and to protect the evaporator from becoming restricted. When the filter or evaporator becomes full of particles, the air does not pass through the evaporator at the proper flow rate and icing forms on the evaporator."

"Mrs. Jones, I recommend that I replace the air filter ($13.00), pump your unit down to remove refrigerant from your evaporator ($22.00), cut the refrigerant lines, remove the evaporator, take the evaporator outside, inspect and service it if required, using an approved evaporator detergent and water ($121.00), reinstall it back into the plenum and solder the refrigerant lines ($39.00), install a new liquid line drier ($49.00), leak-check your system with nitrogen ($45.00), eliminate all the air in the system by evacuation ($54.00), reintroduce refrigerant into the system, and perform a complete service on your air conditioner including the blower motor ($110.00). I also recommend a maintenance agreement with our company ($160.00) to assure that your air filter gets replaced twice a year."

"Mrs. Jones, this is the only sure way I can prevent this from happening again. The unit may be fine by just replacing the filter, but I cannot guarantee that your evaporator will not freeze up again."

This is Mrs. Jones: "Well, let's replace the filter and see if that works."

Service technician: "That is fine, Mrs. Jones, but I would like you to know that our company may not be able to get here right away if your air conditioner does freeze up again."

Make sure you write all your recommendations and prices quoted on your invoice that Mrs. Jones will sign. If she does happen to call in a couple of days, it is no longer a callback and all work will be billable. You have just bought insurance for nothing. I recommend that all suggestions a technician offers a customer, whether accepted or not, be noted on the invoice with the quoted price. You are insured. If a customer calls back because the equipment is still not operating, the technician must reply;

"Mrs. Jones, on our previous invoice I had quoted you prices to repair the problem if your air conditioning system continued to freeze up. I will still honor the prices quoted to you, Mrs. Jones, but I will not be able to be there until Tuesday."

The customer has no choice but to agree to pay. I, personally, do not mind these calls, because I know the prices I have quoted are accepted. If the customers thought our prices were too high, there is no way they would have called us back. They know what needs to be done before they call, because it was on the previous invoice.

And who knows, Mrs. Jones may have approved all of the recommendations during your first visit. Now you have just increased your sales per hour. The technician is forced to do a complete and thorough job. The technician is collecting preapproved money for it, and the customer knows exactly what is going to be done.

I will give you another example of how I have used this technique to prevent a callback. While performing maintenance for a local customer, I noticed a severely pitted contactor controlling the first stage compressor. I had written the recommendation for replacement of the contactor on the invoice along with how much it would cost. When I completed the maintenance of the units, I made sure my invoice was in order and approached the owner. Since I had recorded all the recommended repairs on the invoice, I was able to inform the owner of all repairs and prices for each unit. I explained to him the purpose of the contactor and the need to have a clean set of contacts supplying electricity to the compressor. His response: "I am happy with just the maintenance today!" I do not get disappointed when this happens. My response is, "That is fine. Your maintenance has been completed and you have a list of our recommendations [as I point to the invoice], so if you will sign the invoice, I will not take any more of your time today." After the "thanks for your business" good-bye, I go to my next call. The reason this does not disappoint me is because I know I will be back.

And sure enough, three weeks later I was back changing the contactor. He also approved me to do two other recommendations that were noted on the initial invoice. The customer could have saved money by approving the repairs initially, because now I have to charge him another dispatch fee plus the repair costs. If I would not have noted the recommended repairs on the invoice, I would have heard, "You were here just 3 weeks ago...." You can finish the sentence with your own words; all technicians know what they would be.

I cannot stress the importance of listing all recommendations on the invoice. This technique will increase your efficiency so much that your superiors will notice and ask you, "How in the world are you doing it, because we have three other technicians we need **you** to train." You have just increased your value to the company. More value equals more money. You may have to redesign your invoices to accommodate all the information. For instance, you may have to add a section on your invoice that is titled recommendations. This is not a major expense for the company and will be well worth the money.

Let me ask you again: Would you buy callback insurance for $2.00 per call? No, you don't have to! You can insure yourself for nothing. It costs you absolutely nothing to write your recommendations on the invoice. This is a detailed example of what I do on a service call:

> I inspect the complete system. I find out what caused the problem and identify what could be a problem in the future.
>
> I list on a sheet of paper all of my customers' options for the recommended repairs. This sheet will have the options listed neatly in detail, along with the cost of each option. I am going to show this sheet to the customer.
>
> I start to fill out the invoice. I list the cause of the current problem. Also, in a separate column, I list all

recommendations of work that should be performed today to prevent future problems, with the prices listed for each recommendation.

I hand the option sheet, the invoice with the listed recommendations, and the financing option sheet (you will learn the importance of the finance option sheet in Chapter 11) to the customer. I start with the option sheet. I explain the problem, and what caused the problem, and discuss the options for repair. I explain the benefits of each option and the cost of each option, and answer any questions the customer may have. After I discuss the option sheet with the customer, I review all the recommendations I have listed on the invoice: "Mrs. Smith, while I was performing the inspection on your unit, I discovered some potential for future problems that you may want to take care of now." I explain each recommendation, what damages may occur if it is not accepted, and the cost of the recommendation. Then I review the financing sheet, which will take the question, "How am I going to pay for this?" out of her mind. She will be allowed to choose the option and recommendations that are best for her without having to worry about paying for it.

After discussing both the options and the recommendations with the customer, I excuse myself for a couple of minutes so the customer can have some time to decide. I will clean or dust the outside of the equipment, excuse myself to go to the truck to get a business card— anything to give the customer a few minutes.

Then I come back and address the customer. "Mrs. Smith, were you able to choose a repair that you feel is best?"

"Yes, Chris. After discussing it with you, I believe the third choice makes the most sense."

"Okay, Mrs. Smith. I will make the listed repairs for the third choice. As far as the recommendations, would you like me to prevent any of the possible future problems while I am here?"

"Yes, Chris. I think it would be a good idea to repair all of them. I do not want the unit to quit working in the middle of the summer."

"Sounds good, Mrs. Smith. I will [briefly cover third choice] and make all the recommended repairs."

When I have completed the repairs, I will complete the invoice, explain it to the customer, and go over the warranty information if needed.

"How have you decided to pay for the repairs, Mrs. Smith?"

"I will write you a check for the full amount when you have finished, Chris."

"Very well, Mrs. Smith. Thank you."

It is important to write down all recommendations on the invoice. A technician can verbally recommend any repair to a customer, but it is not as effective as writing it on the invoice. The customer will not remember verbal recommendations, especially weeks after they were made, which means there will be a callback. Mrs. Smith may not have approved any of the recommendations. If her unit fails, I will not be responsible for her decision not to repair it while I was there. It will not be considered a callback if the customer did not accept your recommendation, which would have prevented the unit from failing. Neither you nor the company you work for will be liable for a recommendation that was refused by a customer. But you need proof to show the customer that the recommendation was offered. That proof is the recommendations listed on the signed invoice. There will be no arguments or damaged relationships between you and your customer when you show them they denied the repair. Plus, you will not have to supply free work because of a callback. "Mrs. Smith, the cause of your air conditioning system failing is [cause of problem]. During our previous visit, we had anticipated the [part] would fail in a short period of time and recommended to you that it be replaced. At that time, for some reason, you choose not to replace the [part]. I will honor the price that was quoted to you, but I have to add a dispatch fee and a travel charge." Mrs. Smith knows she should pay for the work. It was her decision not to replace the part the first time, which makes her accountable, not you. Don't have the "I told you so" attitude. Mrs. Smith knows her air-conditioning system is not operating because of a decision she has made. "Mrs. Smith, people make decisions every day believing they are making the right choice. It doesn't always turn out that way. I will be happy to get your system operating at the price we discussed [original quote plus dispatch plus travel] if you would like." Understand the state of your customer's emotions. Mrs. Smith is embarrassed because originally she chose not to accept my recommendation. The decision she chose was the wrong one. I do not need to enforce that. I need to allow her to feel comfortable to buy from me. If I am able to do this, Mrs. Smith will have a difficult time refusing any of my future recommendations. I will continually increase my yearly invoice totals if all my customers have difficulty refusing my recommendations. I will not take advantage of them, but any marginal repairs will no longer be rejected.

CHAPTER 6

THE CUSTOMER

Many service technicians look at the title of this chapter and just skim over it. They do not understand the importance of **customer service**. You can be the most technically talented person in the world, and yet you will not succeed in this business unless you know how to deal with people. "Soft skills" refer to how technicians treat their customer. If you ask any employer what the most important quality is in a technician, the answer will be how he treats the customer. Remember in Chapter 4 when I used the quote, "the old way of doing business"? Technicians cannot use the same customer service skills our industry has used in the past. Why? Because there basically were none. As long as the equipment was repaired, it did not matter if the technician was drunk or sober. Now, before I get a lot of calls, I know some companies have invested and succeeded in delivering quality customer service for many years. But customer service and customer satisfaction is more important today than it has ever been.

True story: I had to clean a condenser on a Whirlpool ice machine that was located at a resort fifty miles from our shop. The invoice consisted of two hours travel and half an hour labor, which at that time equaled $75.00. As the resort owner was reading the invoice, he started to shake his head. These were the first words out of his mouth: "If ole Al was still alive, I could have saved $73.50. He used to drive up here and do this for a beer." Now, I did know Al when he was alive, and the story the resort owner told was probably true, but the electric company will not keep my shop lights on if I just give them a beer. I am sure you will hear many of these stories the longer you are in the field. The point is, just as we must use new techniques for service and sales, we must also use new techniques for how we treat customers.

Here is the problem with customers: They are all different. There are no categories for customers. It would be easy if there were only four types of customers, but that isn't the case. Technicians try to categorize customers. "They were not the type of customer who was going to buy from us anyway" is a common category. Technicians use this for an excuse because for one reason or another, they lost the sale. Why didn't they get the sale? As we learned, they did not show enough value. But it is easier to blame the customer than to admit they need to apply new techniques. Have you heard this one: "I gave him discount pricing because he was irate when I got there"? Why was he irate? Would you like to buy callback insurance? The reason I refer to previous chapters is to show you how they all interlock together. And for every excuse you use, you are losing money.

I have a saying that I use in the classroom to emphasize to our students the importance of customer service. "Every customer is upset when they see me because it means something is broken and they will have to spend money." It sounds bad but it is true. Technicians have to face reality and realize that not all customers are kind and gentle. Some of them will wait for an opportunity to tell you exactly what they think of you. For those of you who are new to this profession, try this one when you cannot figure out what the problem is after trying for three hours: "I have only been in this field for about a year, and I cannot figure it out so I will have to send someone else out when they become available." That's the opening some customers are waiting for. After you say that, some customers will let you know, in their own words, how stupid you are, how stupid the company you work for is, and how stupid the equipment is, and probably will inform you about how stupid your parents are for having such a stupid child.

Technicians also get in trouble by downplaying their role. Imagine you get called out on a Saturday. The customer says that a representative from your company just performed maintenance on the unit four days ago. The wife has the receipt, but she went to visit her mother. No receipt and the dispatcher does not work on Saturdays. You have no idea if this is a true story or not, so you will have to collect. Say this and see what response you get: "I am only a technician. I am not able to make warranty decisions so I will have to collect." Here is the customer's opening: "*only* a technician." You have downplayed your role. This gives the customer the dominant edge in the conversation and some customers will take advantage of it. Here is the correct response: "I am a service technician not in the position to make a warranty decision on a Saturday. I am willing to repair your equipment, but I will have to collect for it today and present the story to my service manager on Monday." What have you just done? You did not downplay your role, which means the conversation is still level. You have offered to repair the equipment on Saturday, but will have to charge for it. And you gave the customer what he wants, an avenue to travel when his wife gets home with the receipt: your service manager. That is the service manager's job, to decide warranty issues. Technicians should not have to worry about it. But we must handle the situation as professionally as we can to prevent the customers from getting aggravated and to increase the chance of their calling your company again. Why? To increase our yearly invoice totals.

A common word people use when asked how they would like to be treated is *respect*. Technicians have to be respectful towards customers, but have to earn the customers' respect. Sound unfair? Well, it isn't. Because every business operates that way. Remember when the business quote for customer service was, "the customer is always right!" Well, it did not take long for that quote to be thrown out the window. It was used so much that customers would remind you of it if there ever was a dispute. The quote is outdated. That quote applied when customers did not mind paying for goods and services. Let me give you an example. You give a customer a bill that totals $350.00. The customer feels it should be $300.00. Is he right? NO! If this happens, you need to show him the value, not reduce the bill. How many times have customers tried to negotiate a bill you have given them? "How much if I pay you cash?" I have always wanted to take these customers' deal, and make sure the equipment would act up again so I could charge them because they have no receipt. And I would wager money that when I hand them the bill they would say, "How much if I pay you cash?" If this has happened to you, I can guarantee that you did not use the shelf method. Remember, the shelf method allows your customers to know all prices before the work is done, so they may choose the option that is right for them.

I have used a lot of quotes, because there are a lot of quotes pertaining to customer service. The one quote that is accurate is the golden rule. "Do unto others as you would have done unto you." I live by this one, because I look at the meaning of it differently from others. To me, as soon as the customer tries to negotiate a bill, he has "done unto me" and my response is, "Mr. Jones, I had quoted you the prices before I repaired your equipment. Prior to giving you the quote, I had calculated the lowest possible price our company could charge for the repairs. I wish I could reduce the price more for you, but I have to charge the price we agreed on before the repairs were made." Mr. Jones knows that the price is set, he agreed to it, and that is the price he will have to pay. He also knows that I handled the situation professionally, and he *will* call our company again and will not negotiate the price again.

Here's why it bothers me when customers negotiate:

A] It makes me feel like a used-car salesman.

B] I am losing money.

C] The customer will continue to use my services and continue to negotiate, which means I will continue to lose money.

D] Why does this customer think he deserves lower prices than my other customers?

E] If I do accept the negotiated price, I guarantee you I still will not get a Christmas card from them.

FRIENDS

Everyone becomes your "friend" when they need you. It's like winning the lottery. That is fine, but some of these "friends" are looking for price breaks. My best customers were my family and close friends. And they paid the same amount as anyone else, without a complaint. Why? Because they knew this is how I made my living. They understood I had to charge them. Do not work for free, ever. People say, "You charge your family full price?" Yes! I have to charge my family and friends because my enemies won't buy from me. I would rather stay home with my wife and kids than to work for free. I could give you a thousand reasons why not to work for free. Here is the best reason of all. It is not professional, and we are professionals. You ever have a doctor work for you at no cost? How about a lawyer? Just the thought of that makes me laugh. Almost as much as when people ask me to work for free.

Here is an example of how strongly I am against working for free. My boss approached me before we started the HVAC/R program at our college and was really urging me to incorporate a 144-hour internship for our students. He felt it to be very beneficial for our students to participate in an internship before completing graduation. I sat down with him and allowed him to explain what type of internship he had in mind. He was really doing well until he spoke these words, " I would see no reason the students would have to get paid for the internship since their time spent in the field will apply towards their graduation." I asked him if he would work 144 hours for free. He chuckled and said he didn't have to and tried to relate our industry to the teaching industry where student teaching is a mandatory, no-pay requirement for graduation. I informed him that as long as I would be teaching the HVAC/R program at our college there would be no "free" work being provided by our students. That goes against everything I teach and everything I believe in, and I will never support such a thing. I stress to you, if you are working for a true friend, they will understand your having to charge them. If they do not understand, you should probably review your friendship. Remember, when you work for a reduced or "free" rate, your yearly invoice totals are decreased. Which means your hourly wage is less than what it should be.

CHAPTER 7
WHO DO THEY THINK THEY ARE?

*W*ho *do customers think they are? We come to their house, repair whatev-*
er the problem may be, bust our butts for them, try to save them money
any way we can, and they treat us as if we are outcasts. How dare they
dispute our bill, criticize our work, and judge our performance? Do they know
how hard I have worked to get to where I am in my career today? Do they know
the amount of time I have spent on a roof when it is 10 degrees outside with the
wind howling around me, repairing a rooftop heater? Do they know the amount
of time I have spent in a 140-degree attic, insulating ductwork? Do they know
how much time I have spent in crawl spaces and basements, on my knees, with
infested little animals crawling all over? Do they know how many nights I have
traveled through blizzard conditions to help people? Do they realize that once
every four weeks, I work twelve days, straight? Do they realize that we have 700
customers and only four technicians? Do they ever consider my working condi-
tions, while they sit behind their plush desk, in their nice, wildlife-decorated "I
am a hunter; view my trophies" office, which I am responsible for keeping at a
comfortable temperature? I cannot wait to hear every detail of their ten-day,
paid-in-full family ski vacation in Colorado. Do they think they are the only cus-
tomers we have? Do they think they are the only call I have all day?

Here is the real question: Who do the technicians think the customers
are? Let's turn the situation around. Imagine you are the customer.

Who do technicians think they are? They are continually late and never call
to notify us. We trust them with everything we own, by allowing them to enter
our home when no one is home, and they leave a mess. I wish they could fix
things right the first time, so I do not continually have to take time off from
work. I wish they would park on the street, so their service van would not leak
oil all over my driveway. I wish they would throw their dirty rags away instead
of leaving them on my furnace. I wish the company would send the same techni-
cians every time, because they are familiar with my equipment. I wish they
would quit trying to convince me that I need a new air conditioner, because I

believe the one I have will last a long time. I wish I could read their invoice so I know what was done to my furnace. I wish they would take their shoes off at the door.

Both parties have legitimate complaints, so let's analyze the advantages for both parties. First, the advantages your customer has using your services instead of your competitors. We will number them individually.

0 – You believe you can do it better and faster than your competitor. (So does your competitor.)

0 – You believe you can do it for less money than your competitor. (So does your competitor.)

0 – You believe you are more knowledgeable than your competitor. (So does your competitor.)

0 – You will guarantee your work. (So does your competitor.)

Not many advantages for your customer. Now, let's look at the technician's advantages.

1 – A paycheck. (Though your check is from your boss, the money comes from the customer.)

2 – Medical insurance. (Do you think your employer pays for this?)

3 – A house or apartment.

4 – Vehicles.

5 – Spending money.

6 – Personal property.

7 – Savings account.

8 – Toys (boats, four-wheelers, snowmobiles, etc.)

We will stop at eight, but as you can see, we could keep going and the technician's advantages would be endless. You need every customer you have, and you need to treat them as if they are the ones that are paying your electricity bill at your house, because guess what? They are! You have to treat them as if they are writing the check for your house payment. Because they are! Each one has to be treated as if he or she is paying for your personal vehicle. They are! It doesn't take a genius to follow the money trail: from your customer's bank account to your boss's bank account to *your* bank account. Without the first deposit, there won't be the last deposit. Without the last deposit, you will not have the rewards listed above.

It's true! Customers do not know the training, the work, the dedication, and the sweat it took us to get where we are. They do not care. I do not care what my banker has been through to get where he is at; I want the money! We have talked about how our industry "used" to be. Customers still have a tendency to relate us as the man bent over in front of a refrigerator with his pants hanging below the butt-crack. Technicians make the same mistake. When someone asks you what you do for a living, do you ever say, " I am a heating man? (Yes, I do know our profession has excellent female technicians, but I am relating this particular example to the popular vote to get the point across.) You might as well have said, "I am *just* a heating man." You downplayed your role.

Here's the problem: The opinion you have of yourself is going to be higher than the opinion your customer is going to have of you. If you think you are "just a heating guy," what is your customer's opinion of you going to be? What is your relationship with the customers going to be if their opinion of you is negative? How much money do you think they will spend with you? We are professionals. We have to feel professional about ourselves. If we do not think we are professionals, no one else will. This is my definition of professional: A person who has the abilities to perform a specialized service needed for an individual in a manner that allows the individual to feel safe, secure, and comfortable. Doesn't say anything about a price! Professionals can charge $10.00 per hour or they can charge $1000.00 per hour. Doesn't say anything about blue-collar or white-collar! We have to be professional.

Let's look at some of the different ways customers find your service. First, there is the search method. The most common search method is the Yellow Pages. Customers search for companies in the Yellow Pages by searching desired categories. Once they have found the category, they find a list of all companies who, because the company is listed under the category, claim to provide the services the customer is looking for. They start with *A* and go all the way down to Z. Keep in mind, they are willing to spend money and they are trying to find a company, which they probably know nothing about, to give it to. Their intent is to spend money and in return, they are looking to get their needs satisfied. Their needs consist of three parts; trust, ability, and respect. That's it. Sure, some will take any company that can get there right away, but it doesn't change their needs (trust, ability, and respect). They know nothing of the companies they are calling and assume, at the very least, they will find ability. They are depending on luck to pick the right company. They are tossing a dart at the board by picking a company out of the Yellow Pages.

Once they find a company, a representative (you) is sent to their house to show or display trust, ability, and respect. If any one of these is missing from your approach, they will not buy from you and they will not call your company again. They missed the bull's-eye! Maintenance agreements are a good indicator of whether the company's representatives are displaying trust, ability, and respect. If you have a lot of agreements that have been in place for a long time and continually get renewed, you can be confident you are satisfying your customer's needs. If you have no agreements or agreements that do not get renewed, you are lacking one or more of the customer's needs. This partially relates to the technicians attitude. Arrogant technician's will not satisfy their customer's needs. Lack of training will not satisfy the customer's needs! And believe it or not, something as simple as a technician's appearance may not satisfy the customer's needs.

I know it is not politically correct to criticize a person's appearance, but I have filled this book with honesty and will not change that now. If you look like a homeless person, you will lack the customers' trust and they will not call your company again. If you arrive with dirt and grease all over you, you will lack the customers' respect and they will not call again. If you continually have a problem repairing the equipment, you will lack the customers' faith in your ability and they will not call again. If all three of the customer needs are not satisfied, their focus switches from getting their equipment repaired to getting you out of their house. Every time the customer does not call, your yearly invoice totals are being reduced and a chance to increase your pay has passed you by.

I had a customer of mine tell me once, "I thought I would use a different company to spread the money around a little bit." He spread the money around because he did not feel our company satisfied his three needs. After investigating it, I noticed that on a previous service call our company was a day late in getting to him and no one had contacted him to let him know. We lost his respect, which resulted in losing his account. A technician should remember customer needs before contacting each and every customer. Technicians believe their services are so dearly needed that all they need to do to satisfy the customer is repair the equipment, which is only part of the profession. Usually, if a technician is not satisfying all of the customer's needs, it results in the customer's calling the company and complaining about the amount of money that was charged for the repair. Unsatisfied customers may feel that even though the equipment was properly repaired, it cost too much money for the services they received. They did not see the value in the price, which means the technician, in some way, did not satisfy all the customer's needs. I include radio, television, and newspaper ads in this category also. Any type of ads that are designed to attract customers who have never used your company's services before are covered in this category.

WORD OF MOUTH

You always hear about word of mouth because there is nothing better than having satisfied customers brag about your company. Who doesn't like to be on the receiving end of a compliment? I am sure you heard this,

"Your company put in an air conditioner for my brother John, and he was very happy with your services." His brother John got his three needs fulfilled by your company, and now he is indirectly telling you he expects the same. The saying is true: If customers are happy with your company, they will tell one to three other people. If they are dissatisfied with your company, they will tell sixteen to twenty other people. Sounds unfair, but as we should know by now, it is not a fair world. Word of mouth can be the most positive advertisement source there is, but it can also be the most damaging. Have you ever had a customer criticize your competitors to you? "I had ABC Air Conditioning over here last year and the thing has not operated correctly since." They have lost their faith in ABC's ability, and are basically begging you to fulfill their needs. If you can do it, you have obtained a customer for life. If you can't, you will be the one getting criticized next year. Fulfill all three of your customers' needs to increase your yearly invoice totals.

There are two reasons why it is important to understand how the customer has chosen your company. Customers who are using your services for the first time is "interviewing" you. They are using your performance to decide if your company is worth developing a relationship with and worth continuing to spend money with. If you lack value in the service, they will think you charged them too much, and they will not use your company again. If they are uncomfortable with you in any way they will not call your company again. If you leave the workplace a mess, they will not call again. If your van has leaked oil all over their driveway, they will not call again. It does not take much to offend first-time customers. If they declined to purchase a maintenance agreement from your company, they were probably not comfortable with you. Analyze what happened and try a different approach on the next first-time customer. Park on the street. Clean your tools. Identify them by "Mr." or "Mrs." Change your approach until you find what works for you. Remember, every customer who does not call reduces your yearly invoice totals and reduces your value to the company.

One thing that never has made any sense to me is a company spending thousands, if not hundreds of thousands of dollars, to attract new customers and little or no money to retain the customers they have. Companies are looking for new customers because they believe they bring in new money. The idea is that new money is better than old money. Believe me, money is money and old money (from customers who continually use your company) costs less and is easier to receive than new money. Customers who continually have used your services are money in the bank. They know you have the capabilities to satisfy their needs. They know they are getting value for their money. They have developed a relationship with your company that they are comfortable with. Don't get me wrong, it is possible to lose these customers if you do not continue to meet their needs, but they are more forgiving than a new customer.

Relate it to when you are the customer. If you need a 1/3 horsepower compressor, you may have six wholesalers who sell it. You prefer to go to a certain one you have developed a relationship with. It does not matter if it costs $20 more, because you know there will be no problems if the compressor fails under warranty. And if there is a question, they will answer it for you. They add extra value into their sale that makes you feel comfortable buying from them at a higher cost. But if you find the wholesaler is not satisfying your needs, you will not hesitate to try to develop a relationship with a different wholesaler. You are no different from your customers.

The other reason technicians should know how they have obtained customers is that you need to understand the amount of money it takes to acquire and retain customers. Advertising is not as simple as buying an ad and then customers call. Customers call only when they need your service, so what advertising accomplishes is that customers hear your company's name so much that when they do have a problem, it is your company's name that first enters their head. That is why catchy jingles or songs tied in with your company ads are so effective. It does cost a lot of money to advertise, usually about 3 percent of the company's gross income, but it is a necessity to operate and to grow a successful business. Understand where your customers come from and the amount of money required to get them, and you will be able to use this to increase your yearly invoice totals by satisfying and retaining customers.

All the money in the world can be spent on advertisement, but if the company and its representatives do not satisfy the customer's needs, it will be money thrown away. I needed an alternator for my truck so I called the local, rather large, dealership to set up an appointment to do the service. I was instructed to bring my truck in at 8:00 A.M. the next day and they would call me when the service was completed. I arrange to have a friend pick me up the next day at the dealership, after I "registered" my truck, to bring me back to my house. Thinking that an alternator replacement should not be a time-consuming repair, I work around my house, waiting for the dealership to call. At about 2:00 P.M., I call the dealership, inquiring about the status of my truck. The service manager tells me, "We have not had time to bring it into the shop yet, but we will certainly give you a call when it is done." I ask him, "Do you have any idea of what time it may be done?" His response: "Not at this time, but like I said, we will call you when it is done." After this discussion, my thought was, "Why would they want me to bring my truck in at 8:00 A.M. if they were not going to work on it at that time?" I was already feeling this dealership was not meeting my needs. They did not mind having me, the customer, waiting all day for a phone call. They had no respect for my day, my time, or my life. At 8:00 P.M. that evening, I call the dealership again to find out the status of my truck. The evening service manager tells me, "Yes, Mr. Reak, we have just brought it in the shop and have began to work on it." I ask him for an estimated time of completion and he says, "It depends on what we run into, but we will call you when it is done." I am really frustrated by this time and know that my truck will not see this place again. Finally, at 11:00 P.M. that evening, while I am enjoying a deep sleep, the dealership calls me and tells me that my truck is done. I go to the dealership that night, and find the only thing that was done was the alternator replacement. I know an alternator replacement does not take three hours. Remember, I called them at 8:00 P.M. and they had said they had just brought it into the shop, and I received a call at 11:00 P.M. saying it was done. I was very disappointed with the service, and feel as if I have been lied to. As I have said, this is a large dealership that spends a lot of money on advertisement, and uses their service department in their advertisements as a benefit to purchase vehicles from them, and they did not satisfy my trust and respect needs. I have faith in their ability, but it is not enough for me to spend any more of my money there. I now take my vehicles to an independent service shop that spends very little money on advertising, knows the importance of my time, and hires ASE certified mechanics. I, as a customer, could not be happier with the services this company provides to my vehicles. They are meeting all my needs, which the other company—spending a lot of money trying to get business—could not do. Advertisement serves one purpose: It gets the customer to call you. It is up to the company and its representatives to get that customer to call you again. The more they call you for service, the more your yearly invoice totals will increase.

CHAPTER 8

PRE-CALL AND POST-CALL

T he technician performing the service, not the dispatcher, needs to make the pre-call and post-calls.

PRE-CALL

When dispatch gives you a service call, do you call the customer before you arrive? I do and there are many reasons why.

Directions. They can inform me of where they are and the quickest way to get there. They are knowledgeable about any road construction, detours, and any other problems I may have getting to them.

Presence. I know they will be there. If you have ever received a message, you know the more people it goes through the less accurate it will be. Customers make appointments in advance, because it usually means they have to take time off from work. A pre-call verifies that the time and place your dispatcher has given you is accurate, and the customer will be there. There is nothing more damaging to your efficiency than to drive all the way across town to find your customer is not home.

Troubleshooting. The customer will explain the symptoms to you, so it helps you plan your approach. This will also save you troubleshooting time when you get there. "The unit operated fine and then the outside fan quit spinning. I can hear a noise coming from the outside unit but the fan is not turning." I have a direction now that I did not have before I called. Troubleshooting is nothing more than a process of gathering information for use to achieve a specific resolution. The customer can provide you with a portion of this information.

Breaking the ice. Someone who trusts you is more likely to buy from you than someone who doesn't. When I call the customer before I get there, this is the conversation:

"Mrs. Jones, this is Chris Reak from AAA Air Conditioning, I understand you have an air conditioning problem that you would like repaired."

"Hi Chris. Yes, we do. It seemed to have worked well yesterday, but now I noticed the fan outside does not spin and wouldn't you know it, my husband just left on vacation. Isn't that how it seems to go."

"Yes, Mrs. Smith, it does seem that is the way it goes. I show you live at 415 Mary Street. What would be the quickest way to get there from Jefferson Drive?" After receiving directions, I say, "Thank you for the directions, Mrs. Jones. I should see you in about fifteen minutes."

What have I accomplished here? First and foremost, she knows my name before I get there. Every viewer liked the character Norm on the show "Cheers." Why? Because everyone in the bar knew his name! I will still formally introduce myself to Mrs. Jones when I see her, "Mrs. Jones, I am Chris and I will be inspecting your problem for you today." "Hi Chris, nice to meet you." I have connected. I have put her in a position to say my name not once, but twice. She now knows who I am!

Secondly, at this point, I have satisfied two of her needs: trust and respect. All I had to do was call her and in a polite, professional manner, introduce myself and inform her how long it would be before I got there, and I have satisfied her respect need. I know, at this point, I have her trust because I am in her house and her husband is away on vacation. I will take care of ability when I give her my analysis and this customer, I guarantee you, will be a customer who will call our company again. I guarantee it! Most technicians who are unable to sell any equipment, parts, or service to Mrs. Jones will lose one of her three needs by the time they present their options. If you track dirt into her house, you lose the sale because you lost her respect need. If you show up looking like a homeless person, you will lose her trust need. Her priority is no longer getting her air conditioner repaired, but to get you out of her house. If you appear to be hesitant or wasting time, you will lose her faith in your ability. The pre-call puts two of these needs at ease.

You are probably thinking to yourself, "Does this guy know how much my cell phone bill will be if I pre and post-call every customer?" My response to you is, "Do you know who is paying for your cell phone?" Your customer is! If making more money is not worth a two-minute phone call on the front and back end of a service call, then stay at your present wage and do not complain. Use a pay phone! A local pre-call will cost you fifty cents at the most, and using a calling card for long-distance calls will reduce your cell phone bill. I just picked up a calling card with 155 minutes for $5.00. This is not a lot of money to retain customers. I will get that money back, and more, when I receive my pay increase. Some companies will even supply you with a calling card. I do not recommend allowing your dispatcher to perform a pre-call or a post-call. The customer will not meet the dispatcher, so it takes all advantages away from the technician's satisfying the customer's needs. The technician performing the service needs to make the pre-call and post-call.

POST-CALL

A phone call after the service call—I personally like to wait a day—is just as important as a phone call before the service call. You have to be smart about it. Never call residential customers at work. Call in the evenings when you know they are not working. If your customers work at night, do not call early in the morning. They will probably be sleeping. If you performed service at a restaurant and are making a post-call, do not call at lunchtime. Call them at a time when you think they will be available. Also, make sure you talk to the same person that you conducted business with. This will help your relationship on your next service call to the customer. You are continuing to extend your confidence in satisfying their needs. You are extending their trust and respect needs. This will be their conversation for the day: "You know, I had AAA Air Conditioning come and look at my air conditioner yesterday, and their technician, Chris, came in, told me what was wrong, offered me six different options on how to repair it, had an invoice I could read, and called me today to see if I needed anything else." The person they are talking to says, "Well, how was the price?" Customer: "You know, the price for the option to repair the unit to operate safe and efficiently wasn't much different from the option for a new air conditioner. So, for an additional four hundred dollars, I received a five-year compressor warranty and a two-year parts and labor warranty. Plus, I have a brand new air conditioner. It was so easy."

The post-call also gives you an opportunity to gain more calls. Has this ever happened to you: "Oh, I forgot to tell you when you were here last time, our walk-in cooler has a tendency to freeze up about every two weeks." Everyone remembers things like this during a post-call. "Our company will be glad to come and look at your cooler. Would you mind calling it into the office, so we can schedule it right away?" You have just created another service call for your company. The more opportunities, the more your yearly invoice totals will be.

Plus, the post-call is indirectly telling your customers that you care about them. You have called them to find out if they are having any problems with the equipment that you have repaired. Wow! That, alone, is worth using your services again. Use a pay phone or calling card to keep the cost down. Just like the pre-call, the post-call will assist you in satisfying your customer's needs, which will increase your yearly invoice totals. A new way of doing business not only for you, but for your customer too. A new way of doing business not only to get you more money, but also to get you more satisfied customers, who will call you again and again for service. I wonder if your competitor is using a new way of doing business or using the same old techniques that have been performed for seventy-five years, back when customers did not mind paying money for goods and services.

CHAPTER 9
THE INVOICE

ll of the previous chapters have discussed ideas you can use to increase your yearly invoice totals by experimenting with what works for you. Here is one you can practice at home with your spouse and kids. Let me ask you, what are the first and last impressions a customer has of your company? Think about that for a minute.

When technicians are asked what is the worst part of their job, most respond that the worst part of the job is the paperwork. The work is done, your hands are dirty, and you have to fill out the paperwork. You are probably late for your next call, which is on the other side of town, and you know all the work you have done will be null and void unless you fill out this little piece of paper and get it signed. Once you get it signed, you have to protect its condition as if it is a bar of gold and you're in an armored truck. That is a huge responsibility, considering most of the time no one can read what it says.

Has your supervisor ever questioned you about an invoice that you turned in two days ago, and the answers you give him come from memory, because you cannot read the invoice? This is an invoice you wrote two days ago, and you have to depend on memory. The only legible part of the whole invoice is in the box to the right of "Total Amount." Service technicians can write numbers fine, but we just can't get a handle on letters. The invoice is a direct replica of a physician's prescription until you get to the total amount. There, in the style of handwriting an author would love to have, lies what we think is the most important part of the invoice, "**Total Amount.**" Actually, the rest of the invoice is just as important, and could cost you and your company money if not written legibly.

Let me ask you a question: How do you or your customers know what is covered under the warranty four months after the service call if the invoice is not readable? Here are the customer's options: Take your word for it that the new repair has nothing to do with the old repair and pay the bill, or dispute the warranty and pay nothing because the invoice is not legible to explain what parts are covered under the warranty. The customer has an argument with you and you have a fifty-fifty chance of convincing the customer that your opinion is the correct one, with no proof to back it up. You are going to lose something, either way you go. The customer who pays the bill will be less likely to call your company again. If you get into a dispute with a business, would you go back to them? Probably not. If you cover a part as in warranty and it is not, you are working for free and losing money towards your yearly invoice totals, which reduces your value. The importance of a neatly written invoice will make you more money and your customers will know exactly what was done.

I learned this the hard way. I received a service call from a guy who was at work, to repair his home air conditioner. He was unable to meet me there, but his wife was at home for the day. I repaired the problem and explained everything in great detail to his wife. The cost of the repair was around $250.00. I received another call from the guy early that evening and he wanted to know what had been done to repair the air conditioner. He said to me, "I see the bill is $250.00, but I can not read what was done." I explained to him what I did and that I had explained everything to his wife before I had left. His wife had gotten confused and did not know exactly what was done. He requested I send a new invoice that he could read. He then, in a very professional manner, said something that has stuck with me. "Your customers' first impression of you is the estimate, and their last impression of you is the invoice. Why you cannot spend a little more time to make these neat is a reason that will eventually lose you customers." I started writing my wife and kids letters to improve my writing skills. They enjoyed them and I can now write neatly. I realize you are reading this and thinking, "Are you kidding me, a chapter on handwriting." Yes! I have chosen to cover all areas that affect your yearly sales invoice. You have to be a complete technician to receive top pay.

Your company gives you an invoice holder for a reason. If you do not know what I am talking about, they are the nice shiny metal containers that hold your invoices. They may also have slots in them for pens, pencils, and a calculator. **Use them!** Do not throw your invoices and/or payments on the floor between the seats in your service vehicle. Do not throw your invoices and/or payments on the passenger seat. Why? Because this is where you throw your partially empty pop cans, tools, parts for the day, Twinkie wrappers, McDonald's debris, and everything else you cannot find a place for. Everything you throw between your seats will damage or stain your invoices and/or payments. If you have ever had to search for an invoice and/or payment by emptying out between your seats, you are losing money. The invoice holders your company supplies to you are made out of metal for a reason—because the inventor knew service technicians would use them! Technicians cannot keep a service truck clean if they were paid to, and the invoices are always on the bottom. We can keep our personal vehicles clean, but as soon as we get a vehicle with decals on it, there is not a dumpster or garbage can to be found. I have always wondered how much money is lost per year because of lost or destroyed invoices. The company isn't the only one losing money, because lost invoices take away from your yearly invoice totals. If you do not turn in the invoice, it does not go towards your total. If your yearly invoice total is reduced, your sales per hour are reduced. And by now you know if your sales per hour are reduced, you are not worth as much.

As far as filling out the invoice, I recommend you put as much information on the invoice as possible. List all your recommended options, along with the price for each. Write down the reason for the complaint, such as "no heat." Write on the invoice all services performed, such as "oiled motors" or "evaluated system operation." Write down all repairs, such as "replaced contactor" or "serviced condenser coil." Write down all information about the unit, such as model number and serial number. This will help you reference the unit for future calls. If they call you next year and inform you that the outside unit is operating, but the inside unit is not running, you can make sure you have the correct fan motor, capacitor, electronic control board, etc. Write down all warranty information on any equipment or replacement parts that have been replaced. Write down all replacement part numbers. Write down as much information you can.

Do not write down "changed filter"; instead write "replaced pleated filter." When customers read "changed filter," it sounds like an easy task and they instantly envision the $1.00 filter from the hardware store. Avoid terms such as changed, cleaned, monitored, and checked. These terms, to the customer, simplify the service performed. Use terms such as replaced, serviced, evaluated, and assessed. For instance, imagine the customer reading an invoice that has "cleaned indoor coil" for a price of $300.00. "Cleaned indoor coil" says nothing about all the work involved in performing the task. Here is my invoice, "pumped system down, removed evaporator from the plenum by cutting copper refrigerant lines, serviced evaporator by completely flushing air passageways with an approved coil detergent and water, reinstalled evaporator into the plenum, resoldered copper lines, replaced filter drier, evacuated and reintroduced refrigerant. Started unit and evaluated the systems operation. Unit is operating fine at this time. High-side pressure is 245, low-side pressure is 72, return temperature is 78 degrees, and supply temperature is 60 degrees." I have done the same amount of work as the technician who wrote, "cleaned indoor coil" but have justified the price to the consumer by explaining the process in detail and using professional terms, such as evaporator (instead of indoor coil). I have, in the customer's mind, done a lot more work than the other technician, which justifies the $300.00 invoice. The customer will not complain about my price, but may complain about $300.00 to "clean indoor coil." Fill the invoice up, and make it legible. It will take an extra five minutes, and will give you a better relationship with the customer and increase your yearly invoice totals. This will also help when you are dealing with just one of the occupants of the residence. Imagine the husband coming home that evening and reading $300.00 to "clean indoor coil."

Purchase orders and shipping invoices are incorporated into a business for a reason. Purchase orders are used so a company can trace and control spending. I will put it in terms you will understand. Allow me to ask you a question. Would you buy a Bose home theatre system for $3500.00 with no receipt? That is the position a technician puts the company in when they misplace Purchase Orders and shipping invoices. I do not know a business, in any industry, that allows their employees to go shopping with a blank check. That is what occurs with lost P.O.'s. You may think you have to order a certain part when there might be six of them within the company. If the company controls spending, your company goals become more easy to reach. Losing money, in any way, shape, or form, is not good for the company, which means it will not be good for the employees. Let me be direct: Technicians are at the bottom of the food chain. If there is less food available for the people at the top (owners, managers, etc.) there will be less food available for the people at the bottom (you). The good news is that technicians are in a position to supply more food to the people on top, not only by keeping track of Purchase Orders and shipping receipts, but also by applying the techniques explained in this book to increase yearly invoice totals.

TIME-OFF

Relate the rest of this chapter to a person you work with. You should be able to place a name with the technicians described.

The highest-paid technicians working for the company. Excellent in the field, usually called by other service techs when they have problems, very selective in the calls they will go on, have a semi-organized truck and messy invoices, and have work listed third on their priority list. These technicians are good people and well liked by coworkers. They have certain accounts that they want no one else to handle. The company usually cuts them some slack on the billable hours because they train other techs, help installers on startups when they have a problem, and have been with the company for quite a period of time. They have been trained not to put importance on the invoice, and don't mind taking time off to spend time with their family or friends. They are comfortable. I have a problem with the invoice (which we already covered) and the priority list.

I have a wife and three kids. I love them dearly and enjoy spending as much time as possible with them. They know I love them. They also know I have two number one priorities: family and profession. Think about it. "I need to take Friday off so I can spend time with my kids." "The drapes for my house will be here at 3:30, so I will need time off before then." No matter what your justification is, you are losing money. Here is my point. Could you afford drapes without your job? Could you buy a nice house, take your kids on trips, buy your wife an anniversary gift, birthday presents, Christmas gifts, pay your bills without your job? Could you afford nice vehicles, boats, and hobbies without your job? Your profession supplies you with your way of life. Would you enjoy taking your family on a vacation if you had no money? Technicians realized before they entered our profession that it is *not* a nine-to-five job. You have to work emergency stand-by, work an occasional Saturday, and work late at certain times of the year. Your job supplies you with so much that it has to be a top priority.

Order drapes in March, not July. Take vacations in September. Sure, it would be nice to take a vacation in the summer, but you're losing money by taking a vacation at this time. And that is why you bought this book—to make more money. Tell your family May, June, July, August, November, December, January, and February are full. That gives you March, April, September, and October to get your "personal" stuff done. Take time off during those months. When you take time off in the busy months, not only are you losing money but you are also asking your coworkers to work more to make up for your being gone. I do not mind people taking time off during the busy season if they are getting "burnt-out," when they have worked so much that it is affecting their efficiency and callback ratio. Now it's costing you money, so take a half-day and regroup. I find that just pulling over to the side of the road, turning my two-way radio off, and sitting for ten minutes does wonders. Gives me the time to regroup and unwind. Then back to it. I will do this two or three times a day when it seems as if the calls are endless.

Sacrifice! Your job supplies you and your family. I can tell you that I have more fun with my family when I have money to take them somewhere. Sure, we have good times at home, but take your kids camping, boating (on weekends you are not working), to the movies, and see how much fun you have. Then thank your hard work and your profession.

CHAPTER 10

THE PROCESS

S o by now you have realized what needs to be done and how you need to go about doing it to receive a higher hourly wage. Keep in mind that I am not an author, I am not a publisher, and I am not an investor. I am a service technician who has found certain techniques that have increased my pay and I am willing to share my techniques with you to increase your pay. I have been on both the employee and employer side of the pay issue and have informed you what it is going to take to get you more money. Ask your boss what you have to do to get a pay increase. Just walk into the office and say, "What do I have to do to earn more money? There has to be a way I can earn more money; how can I do that? Do not accept the answer, "You need to work more hours!" because you are not making more money, you are just working more.

The company should have a plan set up for pay raises, and let me tell you something right now, seniority is important, but it should not determine the pay scale. I disagree that you should get a raise every year because you have been with a company for a certain amount of time. That is not to say I disagree with union shops. There are pros and cons to both. Technicians should get pay raises for successfully passing any certifications that are related to our industry. Technicians should be rewarded financially for improving technical and soft skill knowledge. But the main factor has to be the average sales per hour.

Let me put the writing on the wall for you. If you get a 25 cent-an-hour raise, you have received a "pacifying" raise. A parent quiets a child with a pacifier; an employer quiets an employee with a "pacifying" raise. A "pacifying" raise is just to keep the technician content and out of the office. "Here, I will give you a raise, now get out of my office." You should not be proud of a "pacifying" raise. Do not go running home all excited and say, "Honey, guess what, I got a raise today." You have just received a $500 a year raise. You will work all year, and not be able to make a new truck payment for one month with your raise money. If you are offered a "pacifying" raise, you should check your average sales per hour number because you may not deserve a raise. Do not complain if your numbers are not adequate for a raise. It is no one's fault but your own. The positive thing about it is that you are in control of adding to your numbers. Apply the "shelf" method and callback insurance techniques to your approach. Concentrate on your customers' needs. Develop many reasons why your customers should buy from you. Know and offer all the financing options to the customer. Make it convenient for customers to buy from you so you increase your sales per hour to get a pay raise you will be proud of.

DEFINING GROWTH

A business plans to improve growth by a certain percentage every year. Growth is defined by total sales of the business. If a business does $5,000,000 a year, and wants to improve growth by 10 percent, it must increase revenue $500,000 a year. Where does this improved growth come from? It comes from your yearly invoice totals. A technician must bring in more to allow the company a chance to reach its goals. When a company succeeds in growing, the technicians become more valuable. A 10 percent growth does not necessarily mean 10 percent growth in technicians. They have twenty employees, so 10 percent growth would mean they would have to hire two more. Very seldom does that happen, so growth is definitely defined as revenue. Revenue is measured in dollars. Technicians need to match their company's growth goals. If a company wants to grow 10 percent, all technicians have to bring in 10 percent more yearly invoice totals.

Growth can be accomplished, but here is the problem. If one technician does not reach the goal, the other technicians must make up for it. You may have reached your personal goal, but the company, as a whole, did not reach its goals. Just because you have reached your goal does not mean a guaranteed pay increase, though it usually is reflected in your yearly invoice totals. A company or business is a team effort. If everyone works hard and efficiently, and incorporates the techniques explained in this book, all technicians can reach their goal, which means all technicians can receive pay increases.

Remember in Chapter 3, I talked about the attitudes of technicians and we covered the technician who doesn't care about anything. The technician who shows up continually late for work, does not improve at the technical level, does not attend company functions. This is the technician who usually is the one that does not reach the goal. This technician is preventing the company from reaching its business goals, which is possibly preventing you from getting a raise.

My personal approach is to address this type of technician. After all, this technician is taking money from my bank account. "You will not be getting a raise this year because our company did not reach our growth goals." My answer to this is: Why did we not reach our goals? Who did not reach their personal goals? I want to know! The company is denying me a pay increase because it did not reach its business goals. I want to know where the problem is. I want to know who the problem is. Because once I find out, I can help them. I can teach them the techniques in this book to improve their approach. I can help them improve their yearly invoice totals. If they do not want my help, then I can recommend they find a profession that makes them happy—a profession that does not affect my pay.

Technicians must be honest with their coworkers. Ask me how much I bring in a year and I will tell you. Ask me how much I make and I will tell you. Management does not like that, but we all have an idea what everyone else is making. Here is what management is afraid of: "Bill makes $2.00 per hour more than me and I have been here longer." So what! Maybe Bill's yearly invoice totals are higher. Maybe Bill's callback ratio is lower. Maybe Bill is more valuable to the company. You as a technician cannot concern yourself with what other technicians are making. I do not care what my coworkers make. I care about what goes into my bank account. Just because Bill makes more than me doesn't mean I should be able to increase my personal budget. I know what I need to live on. I know my cable bill is going to be $39.95 every month. It does not matter what Bill makes, my cable bill stays the same. Technicians let their egos get in the way of when the issues are really not important. The thought is, "If I make more than Bill per hour, that means I know more than Bill." They forget it is a team effort.

Put *yourself* in a position that the company does not want to lose you. Who knows, come layoff time, Bill may be the one out the door. Why do we worry about other technicians' pay? Because we want to make sure we are on the right step on the company ladder. The top step is the money technician—the highest-paid technician in the company. One step below the money technician is the second-highest-paid technician; below that technician is the third-highest-paid technician, and it continues all the way down until we get to the bottom of the ladder, the lowest-paid technician—usually the hardest-working technician—in the company. Such technicians get all the attic jobs, all the crawl-space jobs, and all the jobs the technicians above them do not want. They are the lowest-paid, the newest to the company, but most impressively, the least likely to complain. The point is, they earn a living doing things other technicians do not want to do, and they do not complain about it. All the jobs they do have to be done. They do not want to do them, but they do. The ladder position does not mean anything to them. They are valuable to the company, but they are considered to be a liability to the company because of their lack of experience. I have always respected such technicians and will go out of my way to help them. And then, before you know it, they start climbing the ladder. Now the ladder position is important to them. Their ego gets in the way of where their focus should be.

Ask any employer; it is much easier to replace the technician who is on the top of the ladder than to replace the technician who is on the bottom. They can go out and "buy" a head technician from another company. The risk of "buying" a head technician is minimal for a company. People are waiting in line to take a head technician position, but you will be hard-pressed to find technicians who will work in the conditions, and for the pay, of the technician on the bottom. The point is, there are technicians who make more than I when they shouldn't, and there are technicians who make less than I when they shouldn't. That is not my problem, so I do not worry about it. Complaining to the boss and other coworkers will not solve the problem. What complaining will do is create tension within the company and reduce your value because it shows you are not a team player. Focus on your job and do it the best that you possibly can to be as valuable to the company as you can be. Focus on satisfying your customers' needs. Focus on being a team player. Focus on positively contributing to the reputation of our industry. Focus on saving your customers money. If you focus on these issues, and apply the techniques in this book, the money will come. You will be a valuable technician who is receiving valuable technician pay.

Technicians believe that if they keep the bill as low as possible, they are saving the customer money and this will lead to fewer complaints. These technicians could not be farther away from the truth. If I repair a twenty-year-old natural gas furnace which operates at 50 percent efficiency for a modest $200.00, and do not give the customers the option to replace it with a high-efficiency furnace, I have not saved my customers a penny. The money they will spend on gas over the next three years could have paid for the new furnace, and they could have banked all the money they saved after the payback. I have done my customers no favors here, and have actually cost them more money by keeping the bill reasonable. Add in the fact that manufacturers are offering warranties as never before on new equipment, and you can plainly see I did not have my customers' best interest in mind by limiting the invoice amount.

If your goal on a service call is to keep the amount of the bill under a certain price, you are doing two things. You are reducing your value to the company because you will be limiting your yearly invoice total, which will limit your pay, and you are wasting your customers' money. Saving the customer money today and saving the customer money for the next ten years are not the same. Saving the customers money today will cost them more money down the road. If your goal is to keep the invoice total under a certain amount, you are not presenting your customers with options.

Technicians think they have the right to make choices for the repair of equipment that is not theirs. They believe they can make decisions for their customers, without discussing other options. This practice is unfair to your customers, probably costing them more money, and is unethical. No other industry operates this way.

Imagine taking your vehicle to the mechanic's and they repair it without consulting with you first. You have a car valued at $700.00, and they repair it for $500.00 without your approval of the repair. When you go to get your car, they hand you a bill for $500.00 and expect you to pay it with no complaints. Your thought: *My car is only worth $700.00, and they just put $500.00 into it without my approval.* That is what you are doing by not offering your customers options. Believe me, your customers will respect you, and your company more, if *they* have the final say on the repairs made to their equipment. Your job includes giving your customers options and letting them decide what is best for them. Forget about keeping the invoice under a certain amount. This is unprofessional and shows you are not focused on what you should be. This will also lead to an increase in callbacks. *I hear this motor bearing beginning to squeak, but if I replace the motor, that will raise the bill to $600.00 and they will definitely not go for that. I should be able to get another year out of the motor.* You have just convinced yourself that you are doing the right thing, but what you have really done was create a situation that will lose you money and your company a customer when the motor fails in two weeks. You have just reduced your wage in two ways: increase in callback ratio and a reduction in your yearly invoice totals. You have decreased your value to the company. Instead of being an asset to the company, you find you are now a liability. Offer your customers options and let *them* decide what the invoice total should be.

HANDLING CALLBACKS

Nothing is more embarrassing than having to go back and repair equipment that you have already been paid to fix. The company doubts you, the customer doubts you, and you doubt yourself. You must realize that they happen to everyone and you must learn from them. Do not be too proud to ask other technicians for help. I do not care about your ego; I care about what the customers' opinion of your company is. Be honest with your customers. Do not try to hide the fact that you have made a mistake or you do not know the cause of the problem. They can sense when they are being lied to. If you lie to your customers, it shows them that you place no value on the relationship and they will not call you again. Admit your mistake. If you were hurried on the call, admit it to them: "I am very sorry and accept full responsibility for your air conditioner being down again. As you can imagine, this is the busy season and I did not take my time to thoroughly analyze the complete operation of your air conditioner. Please accept my apology. What I have found is that the condenser fan motor has seized and needs to be replaced. I will install the motor and reevaluate the complete operation of your system at no cost to you, but request you pay for the new motor which will be $125.00." You are going to lose some money on the labor, but you will regain that money in the future *if* you are able to keep the customer buying from your company.

If you play hard-ass or lie about the events, and demand the customer pay for the complete repair, you will probably be thrown out of the residence or business and will never be called again. You will never regain anything, plus you will lose a customer, be criticized by this customer to other potential customers, and lose money towards your yearly invoice totals. Your losses will be endless. You can afford to lose an hour of pay to retain a customer. You will get the money back. Try to at least get them to pay for the part, so the company will not lose money. Remember, if the company loses money, it reduces the amount available for your pay raise. The attitude the technician needs to have is to forget about the money being lost on labor, and concentrate on retaining the customer.

By all means, don't give away the farm. I would think your company has callback policies that you are required to follow, which probably request you to do your best to retain the customer. I absolutely hate working for free. But if I overlooked something, or performed unacceptable work that my customer has already paid for, I owe it to my customer to correct the problem and repair any damages that may have been done to our relationship. When a callback happens, I fully expect the customer to be upset and very disappointed. If I were to lie about the events, the customer would be even more disappointed. I would be adding gas to a fire that would escalate out of control. I would never be able to repair the relationship. People make mistakes. Service technicians are people. But people also forgive people who own up to their mistakes. Customers do understand that technicians do make mistakes and that we are human.

CHAPTER 11

COMPANY SUPPORT

T he company you work for plays a key role in the amount of money you are paid. Not only does it have the final say on whether you receive a pay increase, but it can also assist in increasing your yearly invoice totals. We live in a world filled with customers who buy on impulse. If you are not familiar with this term, next time you are at a store in the checkout line, take a look at all the displays placed in the general area of the cash register. These displays are filled with everyday, simple items, such as gum, lighters, gossip magazines, batteries, etc. This is a very successful sales technique, designed to allow you to shop with ease while waiting in the checkout line. You had no intention of buying these items when you arrived at the store, but while you were waiting, found a reason to purchase them. If those displays were not placed in that general area, you and many other customers would not buy the product. No one goes to the store just to buy a gossip magazine. All products are sold because the consumers want them right now. They do not want to wait, because their time is valuable to them.

Companies can help technicians increase their yearly invoice totals by allowing them to present products, write estimates, and sell the job right on the spot. Here is a common system some companies are using that reduces the chance of completing the sale: The technician recommends to the customer a new air conditioning system, the customer asks for a price, the technician responds that a company salesman will get in contact to set up an appointment to review the job and quote a price, the salesman meets with the customer two days later, and the customer has already received two other bids. If this is the system your company has in place, you are losing money. Your company needs to develop a price book and trust you to give quotes on the spot. The price book can be as simple as a three-ring binder that has the installed prices of *all* your residential equipment. When customers ask for a price, I am able to grab my price book, quote a price, draw up a proposal, have them sign it, collect money down and, after confirming with the dispatcher, set up a day and time when the job will be done that agrees with the customers' schedule. They have no reason to shop elsewhere.

When using the price book, keep in mind that not all jobs are the same. But before I quote the job, I inspect the job to verify there will be no costly surprises. If there is additional work, such as drilling a hole in concrete to run the air conditioning lines through, I need to add the extra labor to the amount listed in the price book. A technician can judge if a job will go smoothly or if it will take longer because of certain circumstances. Here is an example: A compressor is locked up on Mrs. Smith's 2-ton air conditioner. The price listed in my price book for an installed 2-ton condensing unit (just for example) is $1750.00. This is the final price, including the 2-ton condensing unit, recovery of refrigerant, new filter drier, solder, evacuation, labor, etc. The technician envisions no problems when performing the change-out. If this is the option that Mrs. Smith chooses, the technician is able to quote the price immediately, let her sign the contract, and give her a time and date the work will be performed, allowing her no time, or reasons, to call a competitor. Now, let's say the compressor is locked up on Mrs. Jones's two-ton air conditioner. She also chooses the option of replacing the condensing unit. The technician notices that the pad underneath the condensing unit is going to have to be leveled. To do this, the technician will have to spend an extra hour on the job. Our shop rate is (for example) $65.00 per hour. This extra hour of labor needs to be added to the price listed in the book. As mentioned, the final price in the book for a 2-ton condensing unit is $1750.00. The quote for Mrs. Jones new unit will be $1815.00. The technician can quote this price to Mrs. Jones, let her sign the contract, and give her a time and date the work will be performed, also giving her no reason to call a competitor. This makes it easy for customers to shop. They do not have to wait or take more time off from work to meet a salesman; they know the day and time the work will be performed and they can "lock in" to my company. Plus, I will also give them a bill for the amount of time it took me to troubleshoot and diagnose the problem of their old system. Having the ability to instantly quote prices for different options allows me to increase my yearly invoice totals because the customer has no reason to challenge the prices and receive other quotes. I give them the opportunity to purchase what they want, along with the cost, right now.

It does take some work for a company to set up a price book. But once it is completed, you can print off copies and give them to all the technicians to carry in their service truck. Price books should contain all equipment your company offers to a residential customer. I recommend that commercial equipment be estimated on a job-by-job basis.

Here is a sample of how to setup your price book pages (prices are for examples only):

R-22 10 SEER

(brand name) 1.5-ton condensing unit   with new evaporator   with new line set
        $1650.00 $1850.00 $1945.00

(brand name) 2-ton condensing unit   with new evaporator   with new line set
        $1750.00 $1950.00 $2045.00

List all the brands separately that you have available for your customers to purchase. Fill the book up with air conditioners, heat pumps, gas furnaces, electric furnaces, boilers, air exchangers, etc...any large item that service technicians will have the opportunity to sell. Create different columns for each, as I have shown above, to include any extras that may be needed like an evaporator or line set. Define the equipment so the technician gives the correct price for the right option, like R-22 10 SEER. Have a separate page for higher SEER and 410-A equipment. Have your company keep it simple, so technicians quote the right prices. Imagine how much money you and the company would lose if your customer wanted a 90 percent high-efficient furnace and you quoted them an 80 percent efficient furnace. Technicians need to be able to sell jobs on the spot. Customers want to buy now, not next week.

Some of you will say, "Hey, that is flat rate!" To a certain degree, you are correct. Understand this: If you are charging by the hour, which is fine, your technicians need to be able to sell equipment on the job, without having to call the office to get a price. This is time-consuming and wasteful, creates confusion, and is losing the technician and the company money. Flat rate or hourly? I do not care. Whatever works for your company. I am not trying to encourage your company to change the way they bill for their time. I am trying to help increase technicians' yearly invoice totals by instantly allowing the customer to purchase equipment from the technician. Do not allow your customers the time to receive quotes from your competitors before they receive your quote. Imagine if you wanted to buy a new set of manifold gauges, and the wholesaler said he would have a salesman call you in a week and let you know what the price is. You are doing the same thing by not quoting the price on the job.

PAYMENTS

Here is the policy I like to work under: All residential customers pay the amount of the invoice when the job is completed. I do not believe it is beneficial to the technician or the company to have open charge accounts for residential service calls. With all the different payment options available (credit cards, check, cash, money order, etc.), there is no reason for them not to pay. By collecting instantly, the company eliminates the chance for nonpayment, keeps its accounts receivable to a minimum, has money for the cost of doing business, and may qualify for a discount by paying wholesalers before a certain date. This will also avoid wasting money paid for interest on loans that may be required because of high accounts receivable. Some customers live beyond their income. Every month they are forced to choose which bills will be paid and which bills will have to wait. "Should I pay my light bill or pay Joe's Heating & Air Conditioning for the work they performed two weeks ago?" Joe is not going to see his money this month! Every customer who does not pay the bill takes money away from the company. The money that is not paid could be the money that is used for your wage increase. Commercial accounts have to be able to charge. Most commercial customers pay their bills on a certain day of each month to keep their operating costs down. Plus, the chances of a commercial customer's not paying a bill are less than for a residential customer.

As noted above, it is beneficial for the company and the technician to accept credit cards. Not only can a company use this as an advantage of doing business with them (*Do you take credit cards?*), they will get paid right away. Let's face it: We live in a plastic-money world. Buy it today, pay for it tomorrow. Credit cards are a billion-dollar-a-year industry and if your company does not accept them, your competitor that does will take jobs away from you. If your company shops around, the money it costs to accept credit cards is minimal. This, again, allows your customers to buy from your company right now, even if they do not have the money right now.

It seems as if everyone involved has some type of financing program available for your customers. Manufacturers have financing, utility companies have financing, and banks will even allow some companies to offer financing to customers directly. Customers can get "ninety days, same as cash," "no interest or payments for one year," "no money down, low monthly payments," and "low-interest home equity" loans. I am sure you have heard of all these. *Use them!* The bottom line is your company is going to get its money, now. Someone else is risking not getting paid, not you. There are so many different types of financing that a customer cannot say to you, "We cannot afford it at this time." A technician has to be informed of all the payment options the company offers to the customer. "Ninety days, same as cash" may not work for a customer, but "no interest, no payments for one year" may. To increase your wage, you have to offer your customer options. Not only repair options, but payment options. All we are doing with the payment option is making it easy for customers to do business with us. Additionally, the company is going to collect the money the customer owes it.

I carry a laminated sheet in my three-ring binder price book that has all the financing options the company has to offer. Here is an example of the outline used and what is contained on the sheet:

Financing Option	Requirements	Approval Time	Interest
CASH	None	Instantly	0 %
CHECK	Valid Identification	Instantly	0 %
CREDIT CARD	Call for authorization	10 minutes	varies
90 DAYS, SAME AS CASH	Completion of form	Same day	0 %
NO INTEREST, NO PAYMENTS, 1 YEAR	Completion of form	Same day	0 %
NO MONEY DOWN, LOW PAYMENTS, 3 YEARS	Completion of form	Same day	12 %

When offering the financing options, I remove this sheet from my price book and hand it to the customers. I allow them to review it and select the best option for them. Notice that the sheet has most of the information on it that they will want to know. It informs them of what needs to be done to apply for the financing and how long it takes to get approval. One item I definitely want on my sheet is the interest charged. If you do not put it on your sheet, you will not be able to answer the customer when they ask. And they will ask. This will require you to call and ask, which will interrupt the flow of your sale.

If they choose an option that requires a form, I get the form from my truck and have them fill it out while I fill out the proposal sheet. Just as for the invoice, I load the proposal sheet with all the information I can provide to the customer about the equipment and the job. I also write on the proposal, "Contingent on finance approval." When the proposal is complete, I review it with the customers and inform them that the proposal is "contingent on finance approval." I have the customers sign the proposal and inform them that I will contact them when I hear from the financing company. I collect the money for the work performed today. When I leave the customers' house, I try to get the application sent in as soon as possible. If I am close to the shop, I will take the time to drop it off. If I am out of town, I will find a place where I can use my calling card to fax it. Most businesses will allow you to use their fax machine with your calling card. Sometimes it costs me a couple of bucks to fax the application in, but that is a small price to pay to increase my yearly invoice totals. As soon as the approval from the financing agency is confirmed, I call the customers to notify them of "the good news" and inform them that I will see them on the day that we agreed the work was to be done. It appears that it takes quite a bit of time to do all this, but the more you do it, the less time it takes. I estimate I spend an extra ten minutes on each call offering the "shelf" method and financing options and properly completing the invoice. Considering what the extra ten minutes does to my yearly invoice total and my wage, it is time well spent.

SERVICE AGREEMENTS

In my price book, I also have the prices for the service agreements. I prefer to call them inspections because the customer is going to pay us to inspect the equipment. If you refer to them as inspections, then the customer is going to be more understanding about paying extra for a contactor or other optioned repairs. The inspections listed in my price book are separated by equipment. The customer has the right to choose any of the service agreements that apply. Here is an example (the prices in the example are not accurate and are used to show the procedure):

Furnace	A/C	Air Exchanger	Boiler	Water Heater	Electronic Air Cleaner
$65.00	$65.00	$25.00	$65.00	$65.0	$50.00

The customers have the option to choose the service agreements they want. If they want their air conditioner, furnace, and electronic air cleaner serviced once a year, the technician adds the price of each to establish the total price. These are just some of the agreements. You can list rooftop units, rooftop units with heat, ductless a/c, window units, etc.

It is a good idea to have a brochure informing the customers what they will receive for the inspection price. For instance, the air conditioner inspection:

- Flush the condensing unit with water (extra charge if chemicals are required).
- Assure correct refrigerant charge (extra charge for any added refrigerant).
- Inspect and tighten loose electrical connections.
- Inspect evaporator for cleanliness (extra charge to flush evaporator).
- Ensure Delta T across evaporator is within manufacturer's specifications.

So on and so forth! Your company should create the list of tasks that the price will cover. At the bottom of the brochure, state that any problems found during the inspection will be quoted and not repaired until the customer authorizes the repair.

As they are selling the inspections, technicians need to inform the customers what they will receive. For instance, "For $65.00, our company will flush the condensing unit with water to remove any dirt and debris restricting the air flow, make sure your air conditioner is properly charged, etc. Now, I must inform you that if anything is discovered during the inspection that we suspect may create a problem, we will quote you the price of the repair and wait for your approval to correct the problem. Here is a brochure that covers all the services that are included for the $65.00 inspection. Any repairs or tasks to correct problems not listed will be quoted separately and will not be repaired until you approve it." I also put this on the invoice that they will sign for the receipt of the service agreement. There will be no questions about what is included and what is extra. There will be no irate customers who think that removing the evaporator and cleaning it should be covered in the $65.00 fee. It is an inspection. "We are going to use our knowledge and specialized tools to inspect your air conditioner to be certain it will operate efficiently, safely, and problem-free until we inspect it again next year. If we find your air conditioner not to be operating efficiently and safely or we suspect it will not be problem-free until next year, we will quote you recommendations and options and let you make the decision on what is best for you and your air conditioner." Inspections are not a hard sale at all, as long as you satisfy your customers' needs. Inspections are not a lot of money, will keep you busy in the slow times, and *give you opportunities*.

This is a perfect opportunity for you to recommend equipment the customer may not know exists. Humidifiers, electronic air cleaners, UV lights, programmable thermostats, pressure controls, hail guards, etc. How many times have you flushed out a plugged condenser and not

offered the customer the option to install a high-pressure control to protect the compressor? How many times have you found a system low on
refrigerant and not offered the customer the option to install a low-pressure control to protect the compressor? Pressure controls are my most
common sale during an inspection, and most technicians do not inform
the customer about them. Installing pressure controls on an air conditioner is going to save the customer money because they protect the
highest-priced component of the system. I offer them both at the same
time: "Mrs. Jones, I showed you the amount of dirt and debris that was
restricting the air flow through your condenser. I have informed you that
this problem could damage the compressor, which will result in a very
expensive repair. I recommend installing a high-pressure control on your
system that will protect your compressor in the event this happens again.
I also recommend installing a low-pressure control to protect your compressor in case you ever develop a leak and lose some of the refrigerant.
The installation cost of these controls is $195.00 [example], which is a lot
less expensive than a new compressor or new unit." Mrs. Jones needs to
have pressure controls. Her condenser has plugged once; it will do it
again. I am recommending she spend a little money today, to prevent her
from spending a lot of money in the future. I am saving her money.

I take advantage of the opportunity that the service agreements give
me. If I notice water damage on the window trim during an inspection I
ask, "Do you get water build-up on your windows in the winter?" I know
the answer will be yes. "I can take care of that for you. An air exchanger
is designed to remove stale air from your house and introduce fresh air
into your house. We can control the amount of air leaving and entering
your home by cycling the system with a humidistat. This will eliminate
the water build-up on your windows, and they are less expensive than
replacing your window trim every three years." SOLD! I am using service agreements to increase my yearly invoice totals. Technicians are in a
hurry to complete the work contained in the service agreements, because
they only cost $65.00. Take your time and look at the system. Look at
your opportunities. Take advantage of service agreements to increase
your yearly invoice totals.

Service agreements can also be used to find out if you are satisfying
your customers' needs. If you are continually renewing service agreements, you are doing a good job of satisfying your customers' needs.
Customers want you to service their units. They trust you, respect you,
and have faith in your ability. If you are having a lot of customers not
accepting them, you are not satisfying one of their needs. There is something they did not like. Keep a record of the service agreements you sell
and renew. Change your approach if you do not sell or renew many. You

are losing money and need to find a new approach to get them to buy or renew the agreement. Selling and retaining service-agreement customers increases your value to the company. You are securing and maintaining a customer base for the company. You will also have less chance of being laid off during slow periods, because the service agreements should be scheduled during the slow times. Service agreements give technicians the chance to increase their yearly invoice totals and keep technicians working during the slow times. As you can tell, it is a good idea to sell these to your customers. Your customers like them because they have a company willing to inspect their equipment before the equipment will be put to heavy use—which, of course, reduces the chance of equipment failing when it is most needed.

CHAPTER 12

DON'T

T his chapter covers a few actions that will *never* get you what you want.

MOONLIGHTING

You want to know the quickest way to lose your job? Work at someone's house after hours with your company truck and do not turn in an invoice. You may be the most sincere person in the world, but keep in mind that this will end your career. Now, I do not mind replacing a fuse for my buddy when I am over at his house for dinner. So what's the difference? Follow these simple rules to define if it is moonlighting or not:

- If your company truck is how you got there.
- If you are nervous about being seen.
- If you are using any company-supplied tools.
- If the repair or installation requires an industry-related part.

If you are taking parts from your service truck, no matter how much they cost, and the company does not receive the money, you have stolen the part. Employee theft is a large concern for employers and they will not tolerate employees who are suspected of it. Keep your nose clean and stay away from employee theft. Do not put yourself in a position to be suspected of this. Where does the money come from to replace the stolen parts? They come from the company's account. The account that also contains the extra money to pay for your pay raise. If you take any money from this account, there is less for you.

If you are nervous about being seen, I ask you: Why? You are probably somewhere you should not be, doing something you should not be doing.

Using company tools resembles Rule 1. The company has purchased these tools to make money for itself, not you. If you are using company tools, without permission, on noncompany-related projects, you have taken money from the company.

If the company bought the tools, they must be specialized tools for the industry. If what you are doing is specialized to our industry, you are moonlighting.

As I have said, I would replace a fuse for a friend, but the friend would have to supply the fuse. I would not replace a thermostat, though. A thermostat is an industry-specific part. A fuse is not. Even if my friend had bought the thermostat at a building supply store, I would say no. A condensing unit is an industry-related part, so you will not see me installing one for my friends unless the work gets billed through the company—but not on the side.

Think about moonlighting for a minute. What is it? Moonlighting is a way customers can save money and technicians can make extra money by supplying service that is illegal in some areas. Who pays the consequences if a moonlighting technician gets caught? The customer? No. YOU! Imagine you charged a customer $100.00 to install a thermostat while you were moonlighting. And you get caught. You have just thrown away a job, a weekly paycheck, benefits, and your reputation, for $100.00. Not to mention an insurance issue! If something goes wrong and results in damage, guess who is responsible?

Think about it: If you do side work, that is money you are taking away from your yearly invoice totals. If you would bill the work through the company, that money would go towards your raise. Moonlighting gives you illegal money now, but it takes money away from you in the long run. Would you like $1000.00 now, or would you like $1.00/hour more for the rest of your working career? If you use an average of 2000 hours a year and a raise of $1.00 per hour, that equals $2000.00 per year. **KEEP FAR AWAY FROM MOONLIGHTING!** Moonlighting will eventually lose you money and cost you your job.

CRITICIZING THE COMPANY

I attended a Scottsman ice machine seminar held in our city about a year ago. If you have ever attended a seminar, you know that every company and HVAC/R person in the area is invited. At this particular seminar, I was sitting at a table with seven technicians who work for a HVAC/R company in our city. After the seminar, while we were eating, two of the technicians started criticizing their service manager, who was not in attendance. It did not take long for the other technicians at the table to offer their opinion of the service manager. I could not believe I was in the middle of this. Even if the service manager deserved being criticized, the company certainly did not deserve it in front of their competitors. Keep in mind, representatives from other companies were in attendance also. I looked around the room and saw a lot of other people looking at our table. They were listening to the conversation at our table. First of all, this was the most unprofessional thing I had ever witnessed, and secondly, no other company was going to hire these technicians, *ever*, because of this public criticism.

After about ten minutes of this, I had enough. I asked the technicians, "If you guys are so unhappy, why don't you work elsewhere?" They all got this dumb look on their face. One technician replied to me, "Reak, you do not know how bad it is there." I said, "I didn't ask that! I am asking why you still work there? If it is so bad that you have to criticize a part of your company in front of so many other companies, why do you still work there?" The look on their faces got dimmer. I continued, "Here's a better question. Why don't you guys start your own business? You can make all the decisions and apply your theories to how a business should operate and then you will have no one to blame but yourselves. I guarantee you, if it doesn't work, you guys will not go to a seminar and criticize yourselves in front of other companies about how bad your decisions were." I then gave them my "support the company and you will benefit" seminar speech and left them all feeling as if they had just insulted their mom. After the seminar, an owner of a different company thanked me for setting the situation straight for these technicians and addressing how unprofessional they had been at the seminar. Everyone at the seminar was aware of what had happened, because they were listening.

I know you and your coworkers go out after work occasionally and discuss issues of concern about the company. That happens in every industry. My advice to you is to discuss the problem with the appropriate person. If you have a problem with the service manager, discuss it with the service manager. If you have a problem with another technician, discuss it with the technician. If you have a problem with the owner, discuss it with the owner. If you worry about losing your job because you have a problem with someone, then you are not valuable to the company. No company will dismiss valuable employees because they want to discuss something that is bothering them about the company. Most companies have meetings regularly to receive input and ideas from the employees. During these meetings, most technicians sit in the back and do not say a word. If you have an opinion that you will more than happily share with your coworkers, please voice it to the people who can make changes—the owners and/or service manager.

CRITICIZING YOUR COMPETITOR

Do not criticize your competitors! I ask you to be a better technician than that. Let your work speak for itself. Everyone has criticized a competitor at one time or another. Look at it this way: All technicians are in the same boat; they just work for different companies. Your competitor is trying to make more money also. A lot of technicians think if they criticize their competitor, it will give them an advantage. This is not true! If you criticize a competitor, the only message you send is that *you* are unprofessional. HVAC/R is a profession that needs everyone to work together.

I will give you an example: It is 10 degrees out and you are working on a Carrier furnace that has a defective electronic board. Your company does not sell the Carrier brand so you do not have a replacement board. Here are your options: A, inform your customer that you will have to order a board and their furnace will be operating in three days, or B, buy the board from your competitor that handles the Carrier brand and repair the furnace right away. You will not be able to select B if you criticize your competitor; they will not sell to you and you will lose the customer. No one wins when employees from a company criticize another company. Your competitor is not limiting the amount of money you are getting paid, you are! If you want to criticize someone, take a look in the mirror.

CHAPTER 13

FINALE

I will assure all technicians that if you focus, concentrate, and use the techniques I have shared with you in this book, you will make more money. Keep in mind it will take some time to get comfortable with the techniques, to find the approach that works best for you, and to prove you are valuable. DO NOT GET UPSET IF YOUR CUSTOMER CHOOSES NOT TO BUY FROM YOU. Learn from it and change or adjust your delivery.

Concentrate on your customers' needs: trust, respect, and ability. You need to understand what customers are looking for. Do not get excited when customers choose an option listed on the "high end" of your shelf. It was their choice. Maintain your composure. You are a professional. How would you feel if a doctor were really excited about selling you a heart transplant? Keep your customer comfortable. Keep the customer and your emotions steady. The biggest fear I have about writing this book is that I will give you the impression that you should sell the customers items they do not need. If you think I approve of that, you need to read this book again. The message is simple: Give your customers options, load up your options with service value, and let them choose what is best for them. Be thorough in your troubleshooting, and do no repairs to the equipment before you give the customer options with the prices.

Technicians need to retrain their minds. It is not your bosses' fault, it is not the company's fault, and it is not the industry's fault you feel underpaid. It is your fault. Figure out your sales per hour, multiply it by .28, and you will find you are pretty close to being paid what you should be paid. You need to accept blame for this. You may be a great technician, but you have not been trained to make yourself a valuable technician. To get paid fairly, you do not necessarily have to work harder, just smarter. Offer options and increase your value to your company. You need to change the perception your company has of you from a technician who is expendable to a technician who is too valuable. How do you become too valuable? Bring in enough money to force your boss not to lose you.

Remember in Chapter 9, I told you that a "head" technician is easier to find than the technician on the bottom of the ladder. You could be the next technician to become a head technician. Let me explain the duties of being a head technician. Not only are you expected to be a great technician, but your responsibilities also include training young technicians and being a role model; continuing education is mandatory, you will be a liaison between the service manager and the other technicians, you may be asked to estimate, and you will be expected and paid to be the best your company has to offer. No mistakes! You will need to be organized. You will learn how to iron, because your appearance will be military. You will get called all hours of the day to assist young technicians who run into trouble. You become a company person, part technician and part management. A technician makes 1000 decisions a day, a head technician makes 5000. You are responsible for most everything in the service department—and all this for more money. It is worth it! It is fun. I do not know a technician who does not want to eventually become the top gun. The reason we are talking about this is because if you do not become valuable now, you will not become a head technician. If you do not become valuable now, you will see other technicians pass by you on the wage scale. And more importantly, if you do not become valuable now, you will continually lose money throughout the rest of your career. Start making money now. Start applying the techniques in this book and increase your value now.

My primary job is to educate future technicians. When I am not teaching, I run service for local contractors. Even though some people consider me a teacher, I am a service technician. I will always be a service technician. I see the damage that is being done by the lack of pay in our profession. I know there is a problem. I read industry-related magazines that have technicians complaining about the pay scale. They put the blame on everyone but themselves. Technicians need to accept responsibility for their pay and find a way to correct it.

I am a properly paid technician. I know what I am worth, I know what I am paid, and dollar amounts are the same. I know my yearly invoice totals, I know my sales per hour, and I know my callback ratio. My boss knows them, too. When I ask for a raise, we break out my numbers and see where I am. There is no debate; there is no criticism. "Here are my numbers, this is what I should be paid, here is where I am, and I feel I deserve a raise!" Now my boss needs to decide. It takes about fifteen minutes and it is done. If my numbers are positive, I get more money. If they are low, I stay the same. Technicians are in a great position. If you have really good numbers, you get a raise. I have never heard of a company that has lowered a technician's wage because of poor numbers. Technicians are either granted a raise or they stay at the same rate. Technicians may feel they lose when their raise request gets denied, but they have not lost anything. Owners definitely lose if they overpay you. The company loses if you are a liability.

Develop reasons why a customer should buy from you. Make sure the reasons you develop are different from what other companies are offering. Separate your company from your competitors by informing customers of the many services you offer. Remember, we sell two things: equipment and service! We gain an advantage over other companies by adding to our services. Technicians need to be allowed to quote installation jobs while they are on site.

Develop a price book so you can give the customer a price, now! In this price book, carry your company's service agreement prices for each piece of equipment and your financing options. Lock customers in for the long haul. Allow your customers to purchase services and products from you with ease. The simpler you make it for them to buy, the less "selling" you will have to do.

Check your attitude. Realize that you are the one gaining from customers' doing business with you. A lot of technicians believe they are doing the customer a favor. This is definitely wrong! Become a team player, use the "shelf" method, protect yourself with the "callback insurance" technique, and keep your invoices and proposals neat and legible. Call your customers before and after performing service. Extend the relationship you have with them. Get all the certifications you can. If you don't, I will continue to take money away from you, reducing your yearly invoice totals. Let me tell you again, I am using this against you.

Continue your education, keep up to date with new products, know your products, and study installation guides before you arrive at the job. Feel free to discuss issues with your employer, who wants your input. Help other technicians with the techniques to achieve the company's goals. Become a well-rounded technician. Enjoy dealing with the customers as much as you enjoy performing the work. And last, but not least, enjoy the money you deserve along with the pride that comes with being a valuable technician.

I hope you will discover the same success I have in applying these techniques in my occupation to become a valuable service technician. If you experience trouble or have any questions concerning any item in this book, please feel free to contact me. I will gladly assist you in anyway I can.

My home phone number is 218-773-1555. Please do not get upset if you are asked to leave a message on the answering machine or if another member of my family asks you to leave a message. I do work away from my home and I will call you back.